INSTRUCTOR'S MANUAL

Laboratory Exercises in

Anatomy and Physiology

with Cat Dissections

SIXTH EDITION

GERARD J. TORTORA
Bergen Community College, Paramus, New Jersey

ROBERT B. TALLITSCH
Augustana College, Rock Island, Illinois

PRENTICE HALL, Upper Saddle River, NJ 07458

Editor-in-Chief: Paul F. Corey
Acquisition Editor: Halie Dinsey
Special Projects Manager: Barbara A. Murray
Production Editor: Lynn Pearlman
Manufacturing Buyer: Michael Bell

Printed in the United States of America

10 9 8 7 6 5 4 3

ISBN 0-13-920356-7

Prentice-Hall International (UK) Limited, London
Prentice-Hall of Australia Pty. Limited, Sydney
Prentice-Hall Canada, Inc., Toronto
Prentice-Hall Hispanoamericana, S.A., Mexico
Prentice-Hall of India Private Limited, New Delhi
Prentice-Hall of Japan, Inc., Tokyo
Pearson Education PLC, Asia
Editora Prentice-Hall do Brasil, Ltda., Rio de Janeiro

Contents

Preface

This instructor's guide is offered for instructors who use *Laboratory Exercises in Anatomy and Physiology with Cat Dissections,* Sixth Edition, by Gerard J. Tortora and Robert B. Tallitsch. The guide is designed to assist you in the following ways:

- Selecting materials that could be used to supplement each exercise.
- Providing students with correct responses to questions asked and to diagrams that are labeled in each exercise.

This guide is organized into four principal sections:

1. **Materials Needed** provides a listing of materials required to complete each exercise. When quantities need to be specified for the convenience of the person preparing the lab, they are listed according to the needs of the individual student, the needs of a group of specified number of students, or according to the number of students that can be served by the amount of a solution to be mixed.

2. **Suggested Audiovisual Materials** contains selected listing of audiovisual materials and sources from which they may be obtained. We hope that these materials will reinforce and supplement the contents of each exercise.

3. **Answers to Illustrations and/or Questions** contains the correct answers to the illustrations that students are required to label and to questions asked within the exercises. Responses to questions asked about student observations or interpretations have not been included.

4. **Answers to Laboratory Report Questions** contains the correct answers to the sections of laboratory report questions at the rear of each exercise. The genetic crosses done in the Laboratory Report Results for Exercise 27 are also included.

Sections 3 and 4 may be utilized in a variety of ways in order to enable students to verify their answers. It should be emphasized that the responses given in these sections are not all-inclusive and in some cases present only one of several correct responses. It is hoped that students will uncover several other correct alternative responses as a result of their research.

Any suggestions, pointed comments, or criticisms of this instructor's guide or of *Laboratory Exercises in Anatomy and Physiology with Cat Dissections,* Sixth Edition, would be appreciated so that appropriate adjustments may be made in subsequent editions.

Gerard J. Tortora
Science and Health, S229
Bergen Community College
400 Paramus Road
Paramus, NJ 07652

Robert B. Tallitsch
Professor of Biology
Augustana College
639 38'th Street
Rock Island, IL. 61201-2296
Internet: bitallitsch@augustana.edu

Distributors of Audiovisual Materials

There are many types of audiovisual materials, models, computer software, and other equipment to accompany lectures and discussions of appropriate subject matter. We have included suggestions for some of these materials in this instructor's guide. Sources for these items, together with an explanation of the code designation for cited sources, follow. Not all distributors are listed, but there are enough to enable the instructor to make a suitable selection. The sources which are listed are either the commercial distributor or a major rental library providing the films/videos on loan. The Kent State University (KSU) Audiovisual Center is featured as a representative example of a large film rental library with national distribution; many other university film libraries have comparable collections which instructors may choose to investigate.

In addition to listing materials according to title, the videos, films, transparencies, film-strips, film-loops, and computer software are characterized when the information is known and applicable, by: running time in minutes; C for color production; and the code designation of the source. The director which follows lists mailing addresses and World Wide Web URL's where applicable. Many sources offer free catalogs on request.

It is *strongly recommended* that all audiovisual materials be **previewed by each instructor** prior to presentation in class to determine suitability, strengths, and weaknesses; this will allow instructors to choose the most appropriate time to schedule showing of the audiovisual materials and will enable instructors to provide appropriate supplementary comments.

Code Designation	*Source*
ABB	Abbot Laboratories, Audio-Services, Dept. 383, Abbott Park, IL. 60064
ACCI	Apple-Century-Crofts, Inc., 440 Park Ave., New York, NY 10016
ACR	America College of Radiology, 20 N. Wacker Drive, Chicago, IL. 60606 http://www.acr.org/
ACS	American Cancer Society, 219 East 45th St., New York, NY 10017 http://www.cancer.org/
ADAM	ADAM Software, 1600 River Edge Parkway, Suite 800, Atlanta, GA 30328 http://www.adam.com
AF	Academy Film, 3918 W. Estes Ave., Lincolnwood, IL. 60645
AGC	Altschul Group Corporation, 1560 Sherman Ave., Suite 100, Evanston, IL 60201
AHP	Alfred Higgins Productions, 9100 Sunset Blvd., Los Angeles, CA 90069
AIF	Australian Instructional Films, 39 Pitt St., Sydney, Australia
AIMS	AIMS Media, Inc., 6901 Woodley Ave., Van Nuys, CA 91406
AJN	The American Journal of Nursing Co., Educational Services Division, 555 West 57th St., New York, NY 10019 http://www.ajn.org/
ALA	American Lung Association, Public Relations Dept., 1740 Broadway, New York, NY 10019 http://www.lungusa.org/
AMA	American Medical Association: distributed by ASF http://www.ama-assn.org/
ASF	Association-Sterling Films, 2221 South Live St., Los Angeles, CA 90007
ATT	American Telephone and Telegraph Co., 195 Broadway, New York, NY 10007 http://www.att.com/

AWL	Addison Wesley Longman Publishing Company, 1 Jacob Way, Reading, MA 01867
BARR	Barr Films, P.O. Box 7878, 12 Schabarum Ave., Irwindale, CA 91706
BFA	Phoenix/BFA Films and Videos, 468 Park Ave. S., New York, NY 10016
BM	Biology Media, P.O. Box 10205, Berkeley, CA 94710
BNF	Benchmark Films, Inc., 145 Scarborough Rd., Briarcliff Manor, NY 10510
BYU	Bringham Young University, DMDP Media Services, W. 164 Stadium, Provo, UT 84602 http://www.byu.edu/home2.html
CA	Career Aids, 20417 Nordhuff St., PO Box AH 98, Chatsworth, CA 91311
CARLE	Carle Medical Communications, 510 W. Main, Urbana, IL http://www.carle.com/
CARO	Carolina Biological Supply, 2700 York Rd., Burlington, NC 27215 http://www.carolina.com/
CARSL	Carousel Films, 260 5'th Ave., Room 705, New York, NY 10001
CDL	Cambridge Development Laboratory, 100 5'th Ave., Waltham, MA 02154
CFI	Counselor Films, Inc., 1740 Cherry St., Philadelphia, PA 19103
CHF	The Center for Humanities, Inc., Box 1000, 90 S. Bedford Rd., Communications Park, Mount Kisco, NY 10549
CHUR	Churchill Films, 12210 Nebraska Ave., Los Angeles, CA 90025
CONN	Connecticut Valley Biological Supply Co., Inc., PO Box 326, 82 Valley Road, Southampton, MA 01073
COR	Coronet/MTI Film and Video, 108 Wilmot Rd., Deerfield, IL 60015-9990
CRM	CRM/McGraw-Hill Films, 674 Via de la Valle, PO Box 641, Del Mar, CA 92014
DA	Document Associates/The Cinema Guild, 1697 Broadway, Suite 802, New York, NY 10019
DIS	Disney Education Productions, 500 S. Buena Vista St., Burbank, CA 91520; distributed by COR
EBEC	Encyclopedia Brittanica Educational Corporation, 425 North Michigan Ave., Chicago, IL. 60611
EBF	Encyclopedia Brittanica Films, Inc., 1150 Wilmette Ave., Wilmette, IL. 60091
EC	Ealing Corp., 2225 Massachusetts Ave., Cambridge, MA 02140
EFL	Eothen Films Ltd., England; distributed by EBEC
EIL	Educational Images, Ltd., PO Box 3456, West Side Station, Elmira, NY 14905
ESP	Educational Software Products, 12 Bella Vista Place, Iowa City, IA 52245
FA	Film Associates; distributed by BFA
FAD	F.A. Davis Co., 1915 Arch St., Philadelphia, PA 19103
FHS	Films for the Humanities and Sciences, Inc. PO Box 2053, Princeton, NJ 08543-2053
FI	Films Incorporated, 5547 N. Ravenswood Ave., Chicago, IL. 60640
GA	Guidance Associates, PO Box 1000, Mount Kisco, NY 10549-0010
GAF	GAF Corp., 140 West 51st Street, New York, NY. 10020
H&B	Halas and Batchelor Cartoon Film LTD., England; distributed by EBF
HIG	Alfred Higgins Productions, Inc., 9100 Sunset Blvd., Los Angeles, CA 90069
HRM	Human Relations Media, 175 Tompkins Ave., Pleasantville, NY 10570
HSC	Hubbard Scientific Co., 1946 Raymond Dr., PO Box 104, Northbrook, IL. 60062
IBIS	Ibis Media, 175 Tompkins Ave., Pleasantville, NY 10570
ICIA	ICI America Inc., Concord Pike and Murphy Rd., Wilmington, DE 19899
IF	Iowa Films, AVC Media Library, University of Iowa Media Center, C-5 East Hall, Iowa city, IA 52240
IFB	International Film Bureau, Inc., 332 S. Michigan Ave., Chicago, IL. 60604

IM	Insight Media, 121 West 85'th St., New York, NY 10024-4401
IP	Iwanami Productions, Inc., 22-2 Kanda Misakicho, Chiyoda-Ku, Tokyo, Japan
ISC	Instructional Services Center, University of South Carolina, Columbia, SC 29208
IU	Indiana University Audio-Visual, Bloomington, IN 47405-5901
JBL	J.B. Lippincott, East Washington Square, Philadelphia, PA 19105
JW	John Wiley and Sons, Inc., 605 3'rd Ave., New York, NY 10158
K&E	Keuffel and Esser Co., Educational media Division, 20 Wippany Rd., Morriston, NJ 07960
KCI	Kalmai Company, Inc., Dept, B6, 21 West Circle, Concord, MA 01742
KSU	Kent State University Audiovisual Center, Kent, OH 44242
LCA	Learning Corporation of America; distributed by COR
LILLY	Eli Lilly and Company, Medical Division, Indianapolis, IN 46206
LL	Lederle Laboratories, Box 110, Danbury, CT 06810
LP	Lawren Productions, Inc., 930 Pitner Ave., Evanston, IL 60202
MAC	The Macmillan Co., 866 3'rd Ave., new York, NY 10022
McG	McGraw-Hill Films. 674 Via de la Valle, PO Box 641, Del Mar, CA 92014
MF	Milner-Fenwick, Inc., 2125 Greenspring Dr., Timonium, MD 21093
MG	Media Guild, 11722 Sorrento Valley Rd., Suite E., San Diego, CA 92121
MI	Medcom Inc., 1633 Broadway, New York, NY 10019
MTI	Coronet/MTI Film and Video; distributed by COR
NAC	National Audiovisual Center, General Services Administration, Washington, DC 20409
NBC	NBC Educational Enterprises, 30 Rockefeller Plaza, Room 412, New York, NY 10112
NDSS	National Down Syndrome Society, 141 Fifth Ave., New York, NY 10010
NET	Net Film Service, distributed by IU
NFM	National Foundation – March of Dimes, Professional Film Library, 600 Grand Ave., Ridgefield, NJ 07657
NGF	National Geographic Films, Karol Media, 22 Riverview Dr., Wayne, NJ 07470
NGS	National Geographic Society, 17'th and "M" Streets NW, Washington, DC 20036
NCS	Nova Scientific Corporation, 2990 Anthony Rd., PO Box 500, Burlington, NC 27215
NYF	New Yorker Films, 16 West 61st street, New York, NY 10023
NYU	New York University Medical Center, Film Division, Division of Center for media Services, 26 Washington Place, New York, NY 10003
PAR	Paramount Communications, c/o Aims Media, 9710 DeSoto Ave., Chatsworth, CA 91311
PE	Perennial Education, Inc., 930 Pitner Ave., Evanston, IL 60202
PFI	Polymorph Films, Inc., 331 Newbury Street, Boston, MA 02115
PHC	Phoenix Film Company; distributed by BFA
PHM	Prentice-Hall Media, Box 1050, Mount Kisco, NY 10549
PLP	Projected Learning Programs, Inc., PO Box 3008, Paradise, CA 95967
PMR	Peter M. Robeck and Co., Inc.; distributed by TLE
PRI	Professional Research, Inc., 930 Pitner Ave., Evanston, IL 60202
PSP	Popular Science Publishing Co., 355 Lexington Ave., New York, NY 10017
PSU	Pennsylvania State University Audio-Visual Services, Special Services Building, University Park, PA 16802
PYR	Pyramid Films and Videos, Box 1048, Santa Monica, CA 90406
QUEUE	Queue, Inc., 562 Boston Ave., Bridgeport, CT 06610
REX	REX Educational Resources Co., PO Box 2379, Burlington, NC 27216

RJB	Robert J. Brady Co., 130 "Q" Street NE, Washington, DC 20002
RPC	Reinhold Publishing Co., New York, NY
SB	Senses Bureau, University of California at San Diego, PO Box 109, La Jolla, CA 92037
SC	Sunburst Communications, Room JT 63, 39 Washington Ave., Pleasantville, NY 10570
SEF	Sterling Educational Films, 241 East 34th Street, New York, NY 10016
SI	Storyboard Inc., 165 East 72nd Street, New York, NY 10021
SIF	Sandler (Institutional) Films, Inc., 762 "A" St., Ashland, OR 97520
SKF	Smith, Kline, and French Laboratories, Services Dept., 1530 Spring Garden St., Philadelphia, PA 19101
SMC	Software Marketing Corp., 9830 South 51'st Street, Building A-131, Phoenix, AZ 85044
SRBO	Sports and Recreational Bureau of Ontario, Toronto, Ontario, Canada
SSS	Science Software Systems Inc., 11899 West Pico Blvd., West Los Angeles, Ca 90064
SU	Syracuse University Audiovisual Center, Syracuse, NY 13210
SYN	Syntex Laboratories, 3401 Hillview Ave., Pal Alto, CA 94304
TF	Teaching Films, Inc., 930 Pitner Ave., Evanston, IL. 60202
TGC	The Graphic Curriculum, PO Box 5651, Lenox Hill Station, New York, NY 10021
TLF	Time-Life Films, Inc., 43 West 16'th Street, New York, NY 10001
TLV	Time-Life Video, 1271 Avenue of the Americas, New York, NY 10020; Distribution Center, 100 Eisenhower Dr., PO Box 644, Paramus, NJ 07653
TNF	The National Foundation – March of Dimes, Professional Film Library, c/o Association, Inc., 600 Grand Ave., Ridgefield, NJ 07657
TR	Trainex corp., PO Box 116, Garden Grove, CA 92642
TSED	Technifax, Scott Educational Division; Out of Business – some materials may be available audiovisual centers or film libraries.
UCEMC	University of California Extension Media Center, 2176 Shattuck Ave., Berkeley, CA 94704
UEVA	Universal Education and Visual Arts (now Universal Pay TV), 100 Universal City Plaza, Universal City, A 91608
UIFC	University of Illinois Film Center, 1325 South Oak Street, Champaign, IL 61820
UMA	University of Minnesota Audiovisual Library Service, 3300 University Ave. SE, Minneapolis, MN 55414
UMedia	University Media; distributed by MG
UPFL	Upjohn Professional Film Library, 7000 Portage Rd., Kalamazoo, MI 49002
USNAC	U.S. Audiovisual Center, General Services Administration, Washington DC 20409
UTEX	University of Texas Medical Branch, Galveston, TX 77550
UWAT	University of Waterloo Audiovisual Center, 200 University Ave. West, Waterloo, Ontario, Canada N2L 3G1
UWF	United World Films, Inc., 221 Park Ave. South, New York, NY 10003
WAVE	Western Audio Visual Enterprises, 826 North Cole Ave., Hollywood, CA 90038
WF	Wellcome Film Library, The Wellcome Building, 183-193 Euston Road, London NW1, England
WFL	Wyeth Film Library, PO Box 8299, Philadelphia, PA 19404
WNSE	Wards Natural Science Establishment, Inc., PO Box 1712, Rochester, NY 14622
WSU	Wayne State University Media Services, Media Booking, 151 Purky Library, Detroit, MI 48202
WX	Wexler Film Production, 801 North Seward St., Los Angeles, CA 91608

1
Microscopy

1. Materials Needed:

Compound microscope
Lens paper
Immersion oil
Xylol or alcohol
Medicine dropper
Microscope slides and cover glasses
Small newspaper print of letters "a," "b," or "e"
Prepared slides of crossing colored threads

2. Suggested Audiovisual Materials:

Films, 16 mm

Fixing and Section Cutting (10 min; C, Sd; McG)
Staining (10 min; C, Sd; McG)
The Microscope (10 min; C, Sd; McG)
Very Small (28 min; C, Sd; McG)

Films, 8 mm

Microscope and its Use (10 min; Si; UWF)

3. Answers to Illustrations and/or Questions:

Answers to Figure 1.1

1. Ocular
2. Body tube
3. Arm
4. Mechanical stage knob
5. Coarse adjustment knob
6. Fine adjustment knob
7. Base
8. Substage lamp
9. Diaphragm
10. Condenser
11. Stage clip of mechanical stage
12. Stage
13. Objectives
14. Revolving nosepiece
15. Nosepiece

Answers to Multiple Choice Questions

1. (b)
2. (c)
3. (d)
4. (c)
5. (b)
6. (d)

Answers to Completion Questions

7. Light-transmitting
8. Microscope field
9. Varies with combination on particular slide
10. Left
11. Less
12. Decreases
13. 1/100,000
14. Photomicrograph
15. 400

Answers to Matching Questions

16. E
17. A
18. H
19. C
20. B
21. G
22. D
23. J
24. I
25. F

2
Introduction to the Human Body

1. Materials Needed:

Textbook of anatomy and physiology
Articulated skeleton
Rubber gloves
Biostat
Anatomical charts showing body systems and body cavities
Dissecting instruments and trays
Laboratory coat
Preserved white rats (male and female)

2. Suggested Audiovisual Materials

Videocassettes

Design for Living (26 min; C, Sd; FHS)
Homeostasis (60 min; C; Sd; IM)
Homeostasis: Maintaining the Stability of Life (36 min; C; Sd; CFM)
Homeostasis: Maintaining the Body's Environment (30 min; C; Sd; IM)
Hot and Cold (26 min; C; Sd; FHS)
Hot and Cold (16 min; C; Sd; FHS)
Landscapes and Interiors (26 min; C; Sd; FHS)
Managing Stress: The Time Bomb Within (14 min; C; Sd; KSU/COR)
One Nation Under Stress (52 min; C; Sd; FHS)
Stress: is Your Lifestyle Killing You? (29 min; C; Sd; KSU)
Stress: Learning to Handle It (23 min; C; Sd; KSU/SIF)
The Million Dollar Scan (30 min; C; Sd; LCA/KSU)
X-Rays and Energy Levels (24 min; C; Sd; KSU)

Films: 16 mm

Basic Anatomy and Physiology of the Mammal: Introduction to Dissection (5 min; UIFC)
From Atoms to Organisms 28 min; C; Sd; McG)
Functions of the Body (15 min; BS; Sd; UEVA)
Incredible Voyage (26 min; C; Sd; McG)
Introduction to Human Biology (26 min; C; Sd; FHS)
Man: The Incredible machine (28 min; C; Sd; NGF)
Patterns of Life: Living or Non-Living (29 min; C; Sd; CRM)
The Human Body; Systems Working Together (15 min; C; Sd; COR/KSU)

Transparencies: 35 mm

Topographical Anatomy (Slides 206-224, McG)
Fundaments of X-Ray Machines 112 slides, EI)
X-Rays of the Human Body (20 slides, EI)

Transparencies: Overhead Projection

Human Anatomy: Biology (2 units; C; 10 transparencies; EBEC)

Computer Software:

Body Language: A Review of Anatomical Terms, Parts I-IV (IBM; CARO)
Flash: Anatomy and Physiology (IBM; PLP)
The Body in Focus (IBM; CA)
Understanding Systems of the Human Body (Macintosh, IBM; QUEUE)
Your Body (Series I and II; CARO)

3. Answers to Illustrations and/or Questions:

Answers to A. Anatomy and Physiology

Subdivisions of Anatomy

Surface Anatomy – Study of the anatomical landmarks on the surface of the body through visualization and palpation.

Gross (macroscopic) anatomy – Study of structures that can be examined without using a microscope.

Systemic anatomy – Study of specific systems of the body.

Regional anatomy – Study of a specific region of the body.

Radiographic anatomy – Study of the structure of the body that can be visualized by the use of x-rays.

Developmental anatomy – Study of the development of an organism from the fertilized egg to the adult form.

Embryology – Study of development of the human from the fertilized egg through the eight week *in utero*.

Histology – Microscopic structure of tissues and organ systems.

Cytology – Chemical and microscopic study of the structure of cells.

Pathological anatomy – Study of gross and microscopic changes in tissues and organ systems associated with disease.

Subdivisions of Physiology

Cell physiology – Study of the function of cells and subcellular structures.

Pathophysiology – Study of functional changes associated with disease.

Exercise physiology – Study of physiological processes in cells, organs, and organ systems as a result of muscular activity.

Neurophysiology – Structure of physiological processes associated with nervous tissue.

Endocrinology – Study of endocrine glands and hormones and how they (hormones) control physiological processes.

Cardiovascular physiology – Study of functions of the heart and blood vessels.

Immunology – Study of body defense mechanisms.

Respiratory physiology – Study of functions of the air passageways and lungs.

Renal physiology – Study of the functions of the kidneys and urinary tract structures.

Answers to C. Systems of the Body

Integumentary:

Organs – Skin and structures derived from it, such as hair, nails, and sweat and oil glands

Functions – Helps regulate body temperature; protects body; eliminates some wastes; receives certain stimuli, such as temperature, pressure, and pain; helps form vitamin D; helps provide immunity.

Skeletal

Organs – All bones of the body, their associated cartilages, and joints.

Functions – Supports and protects the body, assists in body movements, houses cells that produce blood cells, and stores minerals and lipids.

Muscular

Organs – All the muscle tissues of the body, including skeletal, smooth, and cardiac, but specifically refers to skeletal muscle tissue, which is usually attached to bones.

Functions – Active contraction in response to neural and/or hormonal input that brings about movement, maintains posture, and produces heat.

Nervous

Organs – Brain, spinal cord, nerves, and sense organs, such as the eye and ear.

Functions – Regulates body activities through nerve impulses by detecting changes in the environment, interpreting the changes, and responding by producing muscular contractions or glandular secretions.

Endocrine

Organs – All cells and glands that produce hormones.

Functions – Regulates body activities through hormones transported by the cardiovascular system.

Cardiovascular

Organs – Blood, heart, and blood vessels.

Functions – Distributes oxygen and nutrients to cells, removes carbon dioxide and wastes from cells, maintains the acid-base balance of the body, protects against disease, prevents hemorrhage by forming blood clots, helps regulate body temperature.

Lymphatic and Immune

Organs – Lymph, lymph nodes, lymphatic vessels, and lymph glands and organs.

Functions – Returns protein and plasma to the cardiovascular system, transports triglycerides from the digestive system to the cardiovascular system, produces white blood cells, and protects against disease by the production of antibodies and other responses.

Respiratory

Organs – The lungs and a series of passageways leading into and out of the lungs.

Functions – Supplies oxygen, eliminates carbon dioxide, helps regulate acid-base balance of the body, and helps produce vocal sounds.

Digestive

Organs – Mouth, pharynx, esophagus, stomach, small intestine, large intestine, gallbladder, liver, pancreas, and salivary glands.

Functions – Performs physical and chemical breakdown of food for use by cells and eliminates solid and other wastes.

Urinary

Organs – Organs that produce, store, and eliminate urine. Includes the kidneys, ureters, urinary bladder, and urethra.

Functions – Regulates chemical composition of blood, eliminates wastes, regulates fluid and electrolyte balance and volume, and helps maintain acid-base and calcium balance of the body.

Reproductive

Organs – Organs (testes and ovaries) that produce reproductive cells or gametes (sperm and ova) and organs that transport and store reproductive cells.

Functions – Produces gametes for reproduction and hormones that facilitate gamete production and fetal development.

Answers to D. Life Processes:

1. Metabolism – the sum of all chemical processes that occur in the body.
2. Responsiveness – the ability to detect and respond to changes in the external or internal environment.

3. Movement – motion of the whole body, individual organs, single cells, or organelles inside cells.
4. Growth –an increase in size that results from an increase in the number or size of existing cells or both.
5. Differentiation – a change that a cell undergoes to develop from an unspecialized to a specialized state.
6. Reproduction – either the formation of new cells for growth, repair, or replacement or the production of a new individual.

Answers to E. Homeostasis:

1. Stimulus – any stress or signal that changes a controlled condition.
2. Controlled condition – some aspect of the body that should be maintained within normal physiological limits.
3. Receptor – a structure that monitors changes in a controlled condition and sends the information to a control center.
4. Input – information sent from a receptor to the control center.
5. Control center – the part of the body that determines the point at which a controlled condition should be maintained.
6. Effector – a structure that receives information from the control center and produces a response that alters the controlled condition.
7. Response – effect produced by an effector that alters the controlled condition.

Answers to H. Directional Terms:

1. Medial
2. Lateral
3. Superior
4. Deep
5. Anterior (ventral)
6. Proximal
7. Inferior
8. Superficial
9. Posterior (dorsal)
10. Distal
11. Intermediate
12. Ipsilateral
13. Contralateral

Answers to J. Body Cavities:

1. P
2. A
3. A
4. T
5. A
6. P
7. A
8. T
9. A
10. P

Answers to K. Abdominopelvic Regions

Region	Representative Structures
Right hypochondriac	Right lobe of liver, gallbladder, and part of right kidney.
Epigastric	Left lobe and part of right lobe of liver, portion of stomach, portion of duodenum, portions of pancreas, and right and left adrenal (suprarenal) glands.
Left hypochondriac	Portions of stomach, spleen, left colic (splenic) flexure, part of left kidney, and part of pancreas.

Right lumbar	Part of cecum, ascending colon, right colic (hepatic) flexure, portion of right kidney, and part of small intestine.
Umbilical	Portion of transverse colon, part of small intestine, bifurcations (branching) of abdominal aorta, and inferior vena cava.
Left lumbar	Descending colon, part of left kidney, and part of small intestine.
Right iliac	Lower end of cecum, appendix, and part of small intestine.
Hypogastric	Urinary bladder (when full), small intestine, and part of sigmoid colon.
Left iliac	Junction of descending colon and sigmoid colon, and part of small intestine.

Answers to Figure 2.1

1. Controlled condition
2. Receptors
3. Input (information from receptors)
4. Control center
5. Output (information to effectors)
6. Receptors
7. Response

Answers to Figure 2.2 (a) and (b)

1. Frontal
2. Orbital or ocular
3. Buccal
4. Oral
5. Mental
6. Cervical
7. Mammary
8. Axillary
9. Umbilical
10. Coxal
11. Inguinal
12. Manual
13. Pubic
14. Femoral
15. Tarsal
16. Digital (foot)
17. Pedal
18. Crural
19. Patellar
20. Digital (hand)
21. Metacarpal
22. Carpal
23. Antebrachial
24. Antecubital
25. Brachial
26. Thoracic
27. Acromial
28. Facial
29. Cranial
30. Cephalic
31. Lumbar
32. Popliteal
33. Calcaneal
34. Plantar
35. Sural
36. Gluteal
37. Olecranal
38. Dorsal

Answers to Figure 2.3

1. Midsagittal (median) plane
2. Transverse (cross-sectional) plane
4. Parasagittal plane
5. Oblique plane

3. Frontal (coronal) plane

Answers to 2.4 (a) and (b)

1. Ventral body cavity
2. Thoracic cavity
3. Abdominopelvic cavity
4. Abdominal cavity
5. Pelvic cavity
6. Cranial cavity
7. Vertebral cavity
8. Dorsal body cavity
9. Left pleural cavity
10. Right pleural cavity
11. Pericardial cavity

Answers to Figure 2.5

1. Right midclavicular line
2. Left midclavicular line
3. Subcostal line
4. Transtubercular line
5. Left hypochondriac region
6. Epigastric region
7. Right hypochondriac region
8. Left lumbar region
9. Umbilical region
10. Right lumbar region
11. Left iliac region
12. Hypogastric region
13. Right iliac region

Answers to Laboratory Report Questions

Answers to Part 1. Multiple Choice

1. (d)
2. (c)
3. (a)
4. (b).
5. (c)
6. (d)
7. (b)
8. (a)
9. (c)
10. (d)
11. (a)
12. (c)
13. (b)
14. (c)
15. (d)
16. (a)
17. (d)
18. (c)
19. (a)

Answers to Part 2. Completion

20. Medial
21. Pelvic
22. Subcostal
23. Popliteal
24. Transverse (horizontal or cross sectional)
25. Distal
26. Pericardial
27. Hypogastric
28. Parasagittal
29. Vertebral (spinal)
30. Cardiovascular
31. Left lower
32. Lymphatic
33. Metabolism
34. Receptor

Answers to Part 3. Matching

35. D
36. I
37. A
38. F
39. H
40. C
41. E
42. G
43. B

Answers to Part 4. Matching

44.	R	51.	P	58.	N
45.	H	52.	K	59.	E
46.	A	53.	D	60.	O
47.	F	54.	J	61.	G
48.	M	55.	Q	62.	I
49.	C	56.	U	63.	L
50.	T	57.	B	64.	S

3
Cells

1. Materials Needed:

Textbook of anatomy and physiology
Lens paper
Compound microscope
Immersion oil
Prepared slides of:
    Ciliated columnar epithelium
    Sperm cells
    Motor neurons
    Smooth or skeletal muscle fibers (cells)
    Stereocilia (e.g.. ductus epididymis)
Prepared slides showing all stages of
cell division (e.g., whitefish blastula)
Charts and models of the various parts of a cell and stages of cell division
Microscope slides and cover glasses
Depression (concave slides)
Small Pyrex' test tubes (3-5 mL). 2 per student
Large Pyrex test tubes (20 mL). 2 per student
Test tube holder
125-mL flasks
Millimeter ruler
String. 6 in. per student
Dialysis tubing, 4 in. per student
One-hole cork stopper
Glass tubing. 6 in. per student
Beakers, 2 per student
Wax pencil
Filter paper
Funnel
Water bath
Medicine droppers
Forceps
Toothpicks
Hot plates
Acid or caustic-resistant gloves
Cultures of *Chaos chaos* or *Amoeba proteus*
Cultures of *Tetrahymena pyrifornzis*

25 mL of 0.75% Na_2CO_3
0.2% neutral red
0.75% acetic acid
1 g baker's yeast
Dilute detergent solution
India ink solution, diluted 1: 10
Crystals of potassium permanganate
10% sucrose solution (dissolve 100 g of sucrose in 1 liter (L) of distilled water;
    serves approximately 10 students)
Crystals of methylene blue or methylene blue solution

Congo red or red food coloring
Potato
Mixture of powdered wood charcoal,
1 % copper sulfate, and boiled starch
0.01 M IKI solution (dissolve 10 g of water, add 2.5 g of iodine and stir; serves approximately 24 students)
5% glucose, and albumin
Concentrated nitric acid
Benedict's solution (add 10 g of anhydrous sodium carbonate and 17.3 g of sodium citrate to 80 mL of distilled water, heat until salts dissolve; dissolve 1.7 g of copper sulfate in 10 mL of distilled water and add the copper sulfate solution to the first mixture to make up a total of 100 mL; serves approximately 24 students)
Silver nitrate (dissolve 1 g of silver nitrate in 100 mL of distilled water; serves approximately 24 students)
Fresh (uncoagulated) ox blood
Isotonic solution (0.9% NaCl)
Hypotonic solution (distilled water)
Hypertonic solution (3% NaCl)
Petri dishes containing about 10 mL of nutrient agar
Model of a generalized cell

2. Suggested Audiovisual Materials

Videocassettes

An Introduction to Cells (C; Sd; EI)
Cancer: The Genetic Connection (filmstrip on video; C; 1991; HRM)
Cell Division and the Life Cycle (filmstrip on video; C; 1991; HRM)
Cell Motility (filmstrip on video; C; EI)
Cell Motility and Microtubules (30 min; C; Sd; FHS)
Cells Out of Control: The Causes of Cancer (C; Sd; GA)
Cell Structure and Function (filmstrip on video; C; EI)
Cytology ad Histology (25 min; C; Sd; 1990; IM/EI)
Diffusion (29 min; C; Sd; 1990; IM)
DNA and Genes (29 min; C; Sd; 1990; IM)
DNA and RNA: Deciphering the Code of Life (38 min; C; Sd; 1990; IM)
DNA: The Master Molecule of Life (38 min; C; Sd; 1990; IM/EI)
Exploring the Cell; Structure and Organelles (C; Sd; 1990; GA)
Genetic Engineering (C; Sd; EI)
Growth and Change (26 min; C; Sd; 1990; FHS)
Inside the Cell: Mechanisms and Molecules (45 min; C; Sd; 1990; IM/GA)
Membranes (filmstrip on video; C; EI)
Mitosis and Meiosis (45 min; C; Sd; 1990; IM)
Mitosis and Meiosis: How Cells Divide (C; Sd; 1990; GA)
Protein Synthesis (18 min; C; Sd; 1990; IM)
Respiration: Energy for Life (47 min; C; Sd; 1990; IM)
The Architecture of Living Cells: Special Structure, Special Function (filmstrip on video; C; 1991; HRM)
The Biochemical Basis of Biology-Cell Structure and Energy Production (60 min; C; Sd; 1992; CARO)
The Biochemical Basis of Biology-DNA and Protein Synthesis (60 min; C; Sd; 1992; CARO)
The Building Blocks of Life (60 min (2 parts, each 30 min} ; C; Sd; 1991; CARO)

The Cell (29 min; C; Sd; 1990; IM)
The Infinite Voyage: The Geometry of Life (60 min; C; Sd; 1990)
The New Cell (40 min; C; Sd; 1990: IM)
Translating the Code: Protein Synthesis (25 min; C; Sd; 1992; HRM/CARO)

Films: 16mm

Cell *Biology;* Films l-12 (C; Sd; UIFC)
Cell Duplication (26 min; C; Sd: FHS)
Macromolecular Biosynthesis Parts I-IV (C; Sd; KCl)
Mitosis (24 min: C; Sd; 1980; EBEC)
Mitosis and Meiosis. Parts I-IV (C; Sd; KCl)
The Cell-Structural Unit of' *Life* (11 min; C; Sd; COR/KSU)
The Life and Death of a Cell (20 min; C; Sd; UCE)
The Thread of Life (59 min; C; Sd; WAVE)

Films: 8 mm

Mitosis: Animal and Plant; Cell Division: Mitosis (C; EBEC)
The Living Animal Cell; Phagocytosis; Pinocytosis; Amoeboid Movement; Leukocyte Movement; Ciliary & Flagellar Movement; The Mitotic Spindle (All Si; H&R)

Transparencies: 35 mm

An Introduction to DNA and Protein Synthesis Set (78 slides; CARO)
Cancer, the Disease (79 slides; EI)
Cancer Therapy (79 slides; EI)
Causes of Cancer (80 slides; EI)
Cell Biology (NSC)
Cell Division-Mitosis and Cytokinesis Set (69 slides; CARO)
Cell Motility (75 slides; BM)
Cell Structure and Function (80 slides; El)
Cell Structures and Their Functions (20 slides; EI)
Cellular Respiration (20 slides; El)
Chromosome Structure in the Interphase Nucleus (80 slides; BM)
Cytology- and Histology (75 slides; EI)
DNA (20 slides; EI)
DNA and RNA: Deciphering the Code Life Set (150 slides SM/CARO)
Enzymes Set (20 slides BM/CARO)
Enzymes Set (46 slides; BM/CARO/EI)
Enzymes: Regulators of Body Chemistry (151 slides; EI)
Genetic Engineering (63 slides; BM/CARO/EI)
Genetic Engineering Set (20 slides; CARO/BM)
Genetics: How Life Remakes Life (GA)
Inside the Cell: Microstructures, Mechanisms and Molecules (150 slides; CARO/GA)
Meiosis (74 slides; BM)
Membranes (80 slides; EI)
Membranes Set (80 slides; CARO/BM)
Metabolism: Structure and Regulation Set (42 slides; BM/CARO/EI)
Mitosis and Meiosis (80 slides; BM)
Mitosis and Meiosis Set (36 slides; CARO)

Mitosis and Meiosis: How Cells Divide (GA)
Protein Synthesis (62 slides; EI)
Protists; Plant and Animal Mitosis; Living Animal Cells (C; 20 slides each title; H&R)
Recombinant DNA (20 slides; EI)
The Animal Cell (40 slides; EI)
The Cancer Cell (80 slides; EI)
The Cell (80 slides; BM)
The Cell Cycle, Mitosis and Cell Division (63 slides; BM/CARO)
The Cell: Its Structure Set (50 slides; Sd; CARO)
The Chemistry of Nucleic Acids (53 slides; BM)
The Genetic Material (59 slides; BM)
The New Genetics: Rights and Responsibilities (GA)
Viruses and Cancer (69 slides; BM)
Visual Approach to Histology: Cytology (20 slides; K&E)

Transparencies: overhead projection

Cell Division Set (10 transparencies)
Cell Machinery Set (12 transparencies, 16 duplicating masters; CARO)
Cell Motility (20 transparencies; BM)
Cells and their Organelles Set (10 transparencies; CARO)
Electron Micrographs of Cell Architecture Set (19 overheads; CARO)
Membranes (20 transparencies; BM)
Mitosis and Meiosis (36 transparencies; BM)

Computer Software

Cell Structure and Function (IBM, EI)
Chemistry for Biologists (IBM. EI)
Enzyme: A Simulation of Enzyme Action (IBM. EI)
Introduction to General Biology, Disk III: Cells (Macintosh. IBM PC; QUEUE)
Mitosis (Apple, IBM; EI)
Osmo: Osmosis in Red Blood Cells (IBM; EI)
The Cell and Cell Chemistry (IBM PC; QUEUE)
The Cell: Examination, Structure, and Function (Macintosh. IBM PC: QUEUE)

3. Answers to Illustrations and/or Questions

Answers to Figure 3.1

1. Microvilli
2. Mitochondrion
3. Cytoplasm
4. Smooth (agranular) endoplasmic reticulum
5. Rough (granular) endoplasmic reticulum
6. Ribosomes
7. Lysosome
8. Plasma (cell) membrane
9. Nucleolus
10. Nuclear envelope (membrane)
11. Nucleus
12. Golgi complex
13. Pericentriolar area
14. Centrioles
15. Centrosome

Answers to A: Cell Parts

1. Plasma Membrane – Encloses cell contents, facilitates contact with other body cells or foreign cells, provides receptors for chemicals, and mediates which materials enter and exit the cell.
2. Cytoplasm – All cellular contents between the plasma membrane and nucleus in which chemical reactions occur.
3. Nucleus – Contains hereditary material (genes) that controls cellular structure and many cellular activities.
4. Endoplasmic reticulum – Rough ER processes and sorts proteins made by ribosomes attached to the rough ER. Proteins are added to carbohydrates to form glycoproteins and proteins are attached to phospholipids to form new membranes. Smooth ER synthesizes phospholipids, fats, and steroids; releases glucose into the blood in the liver; inactivates or detoxifies drugs and other potentially harmful substances for the liver; and in muscle cells, sarcoplasmic reticulum (similar to smooth ER) releases calcium ions that trigger muscle contraction.
5. Ribosome – Site of protein synthesis.
6. Golgi complex –Modifies, sorts, packages, and transports proteins from the rough ER; forms lysosomes. Transported proteins in vesicles may be secreted by exocytosis, incorporated into the plasma membrane, or incorporated into lysosomes.
7. Mitochondria – Production of ATP.
8. Lysosome – Stores digestive enzymes that participate in autophagy (digestion of worn-out organelles), autolysis (destruction of their host cells) and extracellular digestion.
9. Peroxisomes – Contain enzymes that oxidize various organic molecules. The reactions produce hydrogen peroxide and an enzyme in peroxisomes uses the hydrogen peroxide to oxidize toxic substances, such as phenol, formaldehyde and alcohol.
10. Cytoskeleton – Microfilaments are involved in contraction in muscle cells. In nonmuscle cells, microfilaments form a contractile ring that pinches a cell in two during cell division; participate in the movement of cells during embryonic development and the movement of white blood cells during infection, skin cells during wound healing, and the spread of cancel cells; provide strength and shape to cells; anchor the cytoskeleton to the plasma membrane; provide support for microvilli; and attach cells to each other and extracellular materials. Intermediate filaments provide mechanical strength, attach cells to each other and extracellular material, and anchor organelles. Microtubules help determine cell shape and function in movement such as intracellular transport of organelles, movement of cilia and flagella, and migration of chromosomes during division.
11. Centrosome – Pericentriolar area serves as an organizing center for microtubule formation in non-dividing cells and the mitotic spindle during cell division. The centrioles play a role in the formation or regeneration of flagella and cilia.
12. Cilium – Moves substances along the surfaces of cells (e.g. respiratory tract).
13. Flagellum – Moves entire cell.

Answers to B. Diversity of Cells

1. Ciliated columnar epithelial cell – Movement of cilia transports substances across surfaces of cells.
2. Sperm cell – Movement of flagellum enables sperm cell to move in liquid medium (semen).

3. Nerve cell – Dendrites pass nerve impulses to cell body and axon passes nerve impulses away from cell body; nerve cell membrane is specialized for conducting a nerve impulse.
4. Muscle cell – Cell membrane specialized for responding to an action potential and cytoplasmic proteins (actin and myosin) are specialized for contraction.

Answers to C.1.e. Hemolysis and Crenation

The shape of red blood cells in an isotonic solution is normal, because the amount of water entering the cells equals the amount leaving.

Red blood cells in a hypotonic solution swell and may eventually burst (hemolysis) because of a net movement of water into the cells.

Red blood cells in a hypertonic solution shrink (crenation) because of a net movement of water out of the cells.

Answers to D. Extracellular Materials

Hyaluronic Acid

Location: Between cells, in joints, and in eyeballs
Functions: Holds cells together, lubricates joints, and maintains shape of eyeballs

Chondroitin sulfate

Location: Cartilage, bone, heart valves, cornea of eye, and umbilical cord
Functions: Provides support and adhesiveness in locations where found

Collagen fibers

Locations: All types of connective tissue. especially bone, cartilage, tendons, and ligaments
Functions: Strength

Reticular fibers

Location: Spleen, lymph nodes. and liver
Functions: Forms stroma (framework)

Elastic fibers

Location: Skin and blood vessels, and lung tissue
Functions: Provides elasticity

5. Answers to Laboratory Report Questions

Answers to Part 1. Multiple Choice

1. (d)
2. (b)
3. (c)
4. (d)
5. (a)
6. (b)
7. (c)
8. (b)

9. (c)
10. (c)
11. (a)
12. (d)
13. (b)
14. (c)
15. (a)
16. (b)
17. (c)
18. (d)
19. (d)
20. (b)

Answers to Part 2. Completion

21. Plasma (cell) membrane
22. Microfilaments
23. Nucleus
24. Flagellum
25. Hypotonic
26. Cytokinesis
27. Golgi complex
28. Lysomes
29. Cilia
30. Endoplasmic reticulum
31. Muscle
32. Chondroitin sulfate
33. Reticular
34. Osmosis
35. Dialysis
36. Chromatin
37. Mitosis
38. Brownian movement

Answers to Part 3. Matching

39. B
40. C
41. E
42. D
43. A

4
Tissues

1. Materials Needed:

Textbook of anatomy and physiology
Compound microscope
Lens paper
Microscope slides
Toothpicks
1% methylene blue stain
Distilled water
Paper towels
Prepared slides of:
- Simple squamous (surface and sectional views)
- Simple cuboidal (sectional view), (i.e. cortex of kidney)
- Adipose (i.e. section of skin)
- Loose areolar connective tissue (mesentery spread)
- Dense regular connective tissue (i.e. longitudinal section of a tendon)
- Dense irregular connective tissue (i.e. dermis of skin)
- Elastic connective tissue (i.e. transverse section of an elastic artery – aorta)
- Reticular connective tissue (i.e. lymph node section stained for reticular fibers)
- Hyaline cartilage (i.e. transverse section through trachea)
- Fibrocartilage (i.e. pubic symphysis or tendon-bone junction)
- Elastic cartilage (i.e. section of epiglottis or external ear)
- Simple columnar epithelium (i.e. small intestine for nonciliated trachea or lung bronchus for ciliated)
- Stratified squamous epithelium (i.e. thin non-cornified skin)
- Transitional epithelium (i.e. urinary bladder)
- Pseudostratified columnar epithelium (i.e. trachea)
- Intestinal or gastric glands (i.e. duodenum or fundic stomach)

Charts and models of epithelial and connective tissues

2. Suggested Audiovisual Materials

Videocassettes

Cytology and Histology (25 min; C; Sd; 1990; IM/EI)
Tissues (29 min: C; Sd; 1990; IM)

Films: 16 mm

From One Cell {cancer} (14 min; C: Sd; ACS)

Transparencies: 35 mm

Animal Cells and Tissues I, II (160 slides: BM)
Cytology and Histology (75 slides/cassette/guide; EI)
Histology (100 slides; EI)
Histology of Basic Tissue Types (20 slides: CONN/EI)

Histology of the Blood and Lymph System (20 slides; CONN)
Histology of the Nervous System (20 slides: CONN)
Histology of the Sensory System (20 slides: CONN)
Histology of the Skeletomuscular System (20 slides: CONN)
Histology of the Reproductive System (20 slides: CONN)
Histology of the Endocrine System (20 slides: CONN)
Histology of the Digestive System: Mouth to Esophagus (20 slides; Conn)
Histology of the Digestive System: Stomach, Intestine & Major Glands (20 slides: CONN)
Histology of the Respiratory, Circulatory and Urinary Systems (20 slides; CONN)
Human Tissues (NSC)
Instructional Slides for Physiology (149 slides in 2 volumes: EBEC)
Mammalian Histology Set (149 slides in 2 volumes; EBEC)
Tissues and Organs Set (262 slides; REX)
Visual Approach to Histology; Connective Tissue (14 slides; FAD)

Transparencies: overhead projection

Electron Micrographs of Muscle Set (11 transparencies: CARO)
Electron Micrographs of Nervous Tissue Set (11 transparencies; CARO)
Electron Micrographs of Blood (10 transparencies: CARO)
Electron Micrographs of Vascular Tissue (6 transparencies: CARO)
Human Bone Histology (1 transparency with student copies; CARO)
Human Skin Histology (1 transparency with student copies; CARO)

Computer Software

Flash: Medical Terms (IBM; PLP)
Health Awareness Games (IBM PC/PCjr; QUEUE)
Health Risk Appraisal (IBM QUEUE)
Human Systems Term Tutor (terminology} (IBM; EI)

3. Answers to Illustrations and/or Questions:

(none)

4. Answers to Laboratory Report Questions:

Answers Part 1. Multiple Choice

1. (d)
2. (c)
3. (b)
4. (a)
5. (b)
6. (a)
7. (c)
8. (b)
9. (d)
10. (d)
11. (b)
12. (d)
13. (c)
14. (a)
15. (b)
16. (d)
17. (a)
18. (d)
19. (b)

Answers to Part 2. Completion

20. Goblet
21. Pseudostratified
22. Fibrobalst
23. Mast
24. Chondrocytes
25. Mesothelium
26. Adipose
27. Reticular
28. Elastic
29. Hyaluronic acid

30. Endocrine
31. Compound
32. Holocrine
33. Serous
34. Acinar
35. Synovial
36. Sebaceous (oil)
37. Basement membrane

Answers to Part 3. Matching

38. E
39. A
40. G
41. I
42. K
43. C
44. J
45. F
46. B
47. L
48. M
49. D
50. H

5
Integumentary System

1. Materials Needed:

Textbook of anatomy and physiology
Compound microscope
Lens paper
Prepared slides of:
    Human skin showing epidermal and dermal structures
    Human hairs in longitudinal and transverse sections
    Charts and models of human skin and human hair in longitudinal and transverse sections

2. Suggested Audiovisual Materials

Videocassettes

Integument (29 min: C; Sd; 1990; IM)
Living with Cancer (26 min; C; Sd; 1990; FHS)
Skin Deep (26 min; C; Sd: 1990; FHS)
The Wonders of Plastic Surgery (57 min; C; Sd; PLP)

Films: 16 mm

Regulation of Body Temperature (22 min; C; Sd; EBEC/KSU)
Skin Deep (26 min: C; Sd; 1990; FHS)

Films: 8 mm

Human Skin: Follicle and Hair Growth (both C; H&B)

Transparencies: 35 mm

Integumentary System (Slides l-5; McG)
Visual Approach to Histology: Integumentary System (12 slides; FAD)
Skin and Its Function (20 slides; EI)
Systems of the Human Body: Skin and Its Functions (20 slides; EI)

Computer Software

Dynamics of Human Skin (IBM; EI)
Graphic Human Anatomy and Physiology Tutor: Integumentary System (IBM; PLP)

3. Answers to Illustrations and/or Questions:

Answers to Figure 5.1

1. Epidermis
2. Papillary layer
3. Reticular layer
4. Dermis
5. Apochne sweat gland
6. Blood vessels
7. Nerve
8. Lamellated (Pacinian) corpuscle
9. Eccrine sweat gland
10. Corpuscle of touch (Meissner corpuscle)
11. Sebaceous (oil) gland
12. Stratum corneum
13. Stratum lucidum
14. Stratum granulosum
15. Stratum spinosum
16. Stratum basale

Answers to Figure 5.2

1. Epidermis
2. Dermis
3. Blood vessels

Answers to Figure 5.3

1. External root sheath
2. Cuticle of internal root sheath
3. Pallid (Henle's) layer
4. Granular (Huxley's) layer
5. Internal root sheath
6. Matrix
7. Bulb
8. Papilla of hair
9. Cuticle of hair
10. Cortex
11. Medulla

Answers to Figure 5.4

1. Hair shaft
2. Sebaceous (oil) gland
3. Arrector pili muscle
4. Hair root
5. Internal root sheath
6. External root sheath
7. Hair follicle
8. Matrix
9. Papilla of hair
10. Bulb

Answers to Figure 5.5 (a) through (c)

1. Free edge
2. Nail body
3. Lunula
4. Eponychium (cuticle)
5. Nail root
6. Nail bed
7. Nail groove
8. Nail fold
9. Hyponchium
10. Nail matrix

Answers to figure 5.6

1. Controlled condition
2. Receptors
3. Input (information from receptors)
4. Control center
5. Output (information to effectors)
6. Effectors
7. Response

4. Answers to Laboratory Report Questions:

Answers to Part 1. Multiple Choice

1. (c)
2. (b)
3. (c)
4. (c)
5. (c)
6. (a)
7. (d)
8. (d)
9. (a)
10. (b)
11. (d)
12. (a)
13. (d)
14. (b)
15. (b)

Answers to Part 2. Completion

16. Organ
17. Epidermis
18. Subcutaneous layer (superficial fascia)
19. System
20. Lucidum
21. Basale
22. Arrector pili
23. Albinism
24. Lamellated (Pacinian)
25. Medulla
26. Papilla of hair
27. Ceruminous
28. Lunula
29. Perspiration
30. Melanocytes
31. Sudoriferous (sweat)

6
Bone Tissue

1. Materials Needed:

Textbook of anatomy and physiology
Compound microscope
Lens paper
Fresh beef bone
Frontal section of a long bone
Bone that has been baked
Bone that has been soaked in nitric acid
Models. charts. and slides of the gross structure of a long bone
Models, charts, and slides of the microscopic structure of compact bone tissue
Articulated skeleton
Disarticulated long, short, flat, and irregular bones
Beauchene skull
Prepared slides of:
    Transverse section of compact bone tissue
    Longitudinal section of compact bone tissue

2. Suggested Audiovisual Materials

Videocassettes

Bones and Movement (9 min; 1990; KSU)
The Human Body: What Can Go Wrong? (six filmstrips on videocassette with guide; EI)

Films: 16 mm

Human Body: Skeleton (10 min; C; Sd; CFI)
How the Body Moves: The Skeleton (20 min; BW; Sd; PMR)

Transparencies: 35 mm

Burns, Fractures and Accidents (Sound slides; CFH)
Histology of the Skeletomuscular System (EI)
Skeletal System and Its Functions (20 slides; EI)

Transparencies: overhead projection

Skeletal System (HSC)

Computer Software

Dynamics of the Human Skeletal System (IBM; EI)
Flash; Bones and Joints (IBM; PLP)
Graphic Human Anatomy and Physiology tutor; Skeletal System (IBM; PLP)
Skeletal System [part of "Body Language: Study of Human Anatomy" series, including figures adapted from *Principles of Anatomy and Physiology,* 6'th ed., by Tortora and Anagnostakos] (IBM; PLP)
Support, Locomotion, and Behavior (IBM, Macintosh; QUEUE)

3. Answers to Illustrations and/or Questions:

Answers to Figure 6.1

1. Articular cartilage
2. Compact bone tissue
3. Periosteum
4. Distal epiphysis
5. Medullary (marrow) cavity
6. Endosteum
7. Diaphysis
8. Spongy bone tissue
9. Proximal epiphysis

Answers to Figure 6.2

1. Osteocyte
2. Central (Haversian) canal
3. Concentric lamellae
4. Perforating (Volkman's) canal
5. Spongy bone tissue
6. Compact bone tissue
7. Canaliculi
8. Lacuna

Answers to Figure 6.3

1. Zone of resting cartilage
2. Zone of proliferating cartilage
3. Zone of hypertrophic cartilage
4. Zone of calcified cartilage

Answers to Figure 6.4

1. Comminuted fracture
2. Colles' fracture
3. Impacted fracture
4. Pott's fracture
5. Greenstick fracture
6. Open fracture

Answers to G. Fractures

Table 6.1 Summary of Selected Fractures

Type of Fracture	*Definition*
Partial	The break across the bone is incomplete.
Complete	The break across the bone is complete, so that the bone is broken into two or more pieces.
Closed (simple)	The bone does not break through the skin.
Open (compound)	The broken ends of the bone protrude through the skin.
Comminuted	The bone has splintered at the site of impact, and smaller fragments of the bone lie between the two main fragments.
Greenstick	A partial fracture in which one side of the bone is broken and the other side bends; occurs only in children.
Spiral	The bone is twisted apart.
Transverse	A fracture at right angles to the longitudinal axis of the bone.
Impacted	One fragment is firmly driven into the other.
Displaced	The anatomical alignment of the bone fragments is not preserved.
Nondisplaced	The anatomical alignment of the bone fragments is preserved.
Stress	Microscopic fractures resulting from inability to withstand repeated stress. They are usually the result of repeated impact activities, such as running, basketball, jumping or aerobic dancing. Approximately 25% of all stress fractures involve the tibia.
Pathologic	Weakening of a bone caused by disease processes such as neoplasia, osteomyelitis, osteoporosis, or osteomalacia.
Pott's	A fracture of the distal end of the fibula, with serious injury of the distal tibial articulation.
Colles'	A fracture of the distal end of the radius in which the distal fragment is displaced posteriorly.

Answers to H. Types of Bones

1. Long: Humerus, ulna, radius, metacarpals, phalanges, femur, tibia, fibula, metatarsals.
2. Short: Carpals, tarsals.
3. Flat: Cranial bones, sternum, ribs, clavicles, scapulas, hip bones.
4. Irregular: Facial bones, vertebrae.

Answers to I. Bone Surface Markings

Marking	*Description*
Depressions and Openings	
fissure	A narrow, cleft-like opening between adjacent parts of bones through which blood vessels or nerves may pass.
foramen	A perforation through a bone through which nerves, blood vessels or ligaments may pass; the end of a canal.
meatus	A passageway; a large foramen; used particularly for an external opening of a canal.
sulcus	A groove or furrow that may accommodate a soft structure such as a blood vessel, nerve, or tendon.
fossa	A shallow depression.
Processes	
Projections That Form Joints	
condyle	A large, rounded, articular eminence.
head	A large, rounded, articular projection supported on the constricted portion (neck) of a bone.
facet	A smooth, flat or nearly flat articular surface.
ramus	Branch.
Projections To Which Tendons, Ligaments, and Other Connective Tissues Attach	
Tubercle	A nodular process; a small rounded eminence.
Tuberosity	A large, often rough, eminence. (Often used synonymously with tubercle.)
Trochanter	Each of two processes below the neck of a femur; a nodular process with a flat top; a small, rounded eminence with a flat top.
Crest	A bony ridge.
Line	A slight ridge.
Spinous process (spine)	A sharp process.
Epicondyle	A ridge above a condyle.

4. Answers to Laboratory Report Questions:

Answers to Part 1. Multiple Choice

1. Sutural
2. Osteocyte
3. Perforating (Volkmann's)
4. Epiphysis
5. Short
6. Medullary (marrow)
7. Articular
8. Canaliculi
9. Periosteum
10. Diaphysis
11. Lamella
12. Endosteum
13. Osseous
14. Metaphysis
15. Osteon (Haversian system)
16. Tricalcium phosphate (hydroxyapatite)
17. Ossification
18. Calcified cartilage
19. Appositional
20. Resorption
21. Endochondrial
22. Hypertrophic
23. Fracture
24. Trabeculae
25. Irregular

7
Bones

1. Materials Needed:

Textbook of anatomy and physiology
Unsectioned articulated skull
Articulated skull in midsaggital section
Beauchene skull
Skull of newborn infant showing fontanels
Skull sectioned to show paranasal sinuses
Male and female articulated skeletons
Disarticulated skeleton
Charts of the skeletal system
Mounted, articulated cat skeleton

2. Suggested Audiovisual Materials

Videocassettes

Preventing Back Injuries (24 min; C; Sd; KSU)
Anatomy of the Upper Limbs (52 min; C; Sd; CARO)

Films

Primary Cancer of the Bone (21 min; API)
Skeletal System (12 min; COR/KSU)

Transparencies: 35 mm

Anatomy of the Skull. Parts I-IV (310 slides; BM)
Anatomy of the Thorax (80 slides; BM)
Anatomy of the Vertebral Column (80 slides; BM)
Skeletal System and Its Function (20 slides; EI/CARO)
A Visual Approach to Histology: Musculoskeletal System (18 slides; FAD)
Anatomy of the Lower Limbs (80 slides; BM)
Anatomy of the Upper Limbs (80 slides; BM)
X-Rays of the Human Body (20 slides; EI)

Transparencies: overhead projection

Skeletal System: Unit 2 (C, 27 transparencies, RJB)
Skeletal System (Trs. 6 – 31; McG)
Skeleton and Muscles (6 transparencies with 10 overlays; CARO)

Computer Software

Body Language: Skeletal System {anatomy} (IBM, Macintosh; PLP)
Bone Probe (Apple; PLP)
Dynamics of the Human Skeletal System (IBM; PLP)

Flash: Bones and Joints (IBM, PLP)
Support, Locomotion and Behavior (IBM, Macintosh; QUEUE)

3. Answers to Illustrations and/or Questions:

Answers to Table 7.1 Summary of Foramina of the Skull

Foramen	*Structures Passing Through*
Carotid	Internal carotid artery
Hypoglossal	Cranial nerve XII (hypoglossal) and branch of ascending pharyngeal artery
Inferior orbital	Maxillary branch of cranial nerve V (trigeminal), zygomatic nerve, and infraorbital vessels
Jugular	Internal jugular vein, cranial nerves IX (glossopharyngeal), X (vagus), and XI (accessory)
Magnum	Medulla oblongata and its meninges, cranial nerve XI (accessory), and vertebral and spinal arteries
Mandibular	Inferior alveolar nerve and vessels
Mastoid	Emissary vein to transverse sinus and branch of occipital artery to dura mater
Mental	Mental nerve and vessels
Olfactory	Cranial nerve I (olfactory)
Optic	Cranial nerve II (optic) and opthalamic artery
Ovale	Mandibular branch of cranial nerve V (trigeminal)
Rotundum	Maxillary branch of cranial nerve V (trigeminal)
Stylomastoid	Cranial nerve VII (facial) and stylomastoid artery
Superior orbital	Cranial nerves III (oculomotor), IV (trochlear), opthalmic branch of V (trigeminal) and VI (abducens)

Answers to Figure 7.5

1. Ethmoidal sinus
2. Frontal sinus
3. Maxillary sinus
4. Sphenoidal sinus

Answers to figure 7.6 (a)

1. Cervical vertebrae
2. Thoracic vertebrae
3. Lumbar vertebrae
4. Sacrum
5. Coccyx

Answers to figure 7.6 (b)

6. Cervical curve
7. Thoracic curve
8. Lumbar curve
9. Sacral curve

Answers to figure 7.7 (a)

1. Spinous process
2. Superior articular facet
3. Vertebral foramen
4. Body
5. Pedicle
6. Lamina
7. Vertebral arch
8. Transverse process

Answers to figure 7.7 (b)

1. Transverse process
2. Lateral mass
3. Superior articular facet
4. Anterior arch
5. Vertebral foramen
6. Transverse foramen
7. Posterior arch

Answers to figure 7.7 (c)

1. Dens
2. Superior articular facet
3. Transverse process
4. Inferior articular facet
5. Body
6. Lateral mass

Answers to figure 7.7 (d)

1. Bifid spinous process
2. Lamina
3. Inferior articular process
4. Superior articular process
5. Body
6. Transverse foramen
7. Transverse process
8. Pedicle
9. Vertebral foramen

Answers to Figure 7.7 (e)

1. Spinous process
2. Superior articular facet
3. Body
4. Vertebral foramen
5. Pedicle
6. Lamina
7. Transverse process
8. Facet for tubercle of rib

Answers to Figure 7.7 (f)

1. Spinous process
2. Superior articular facet
3. Vertebral foramen
4. Body
5. Pedicle
6. Transverse process
7. Lamina

Answers to Figure 7.7 (g) and (h)

1. Sacral promontory
2. Transverse line
3. Coccyx
4. Anterior sacral foramen
5. Sacral canal
6. Auricular surface
7. Lateral sacral crest
8. Median sacral crest

5. Sacral canal
10. Dorsal sacral foramen

Answers to figure 7.8 (a)

1. Suprasternal notch
2. Costal cartilage
3. Xiphoid process
4. Body
5. Manubrium
6. Clavicular notch

Answers to figure 7.8 (b)

1. Superior facet
2. Neck
3. Head
4. Inferior facet
5. Articular part of tubercle
6. Body
7. Costal groove

Answers to figure 7.9 (a)

1. Sternal extremity
2. Conoid tubercle
2. Acromial extremity

Answers to figure 7.9 (b)

1. Acromion
2. Coracoid process
3. Superior border
4. Body
5. Superior angle
6. Medial (vertebral) border
7. Lateral (axillary) border
8. Inferior angle
9. Glenoid cavity

Answers to Figure 7.9 (c)

1. Coracoid process
2. Acromion
3. Inferior angle
4. Lateral (axillary) border
5. Medial (vertebral) border
6. Body
7. Infraspinous fossa
8. Supraspinous fossa
9. Superior angle
10. Spine
11. Superior border

Answers to Figure 7.9 (d)

1. Acromion
2. Coracoid process
3. Spine
4. Glenoid cavity
5. Body
6. Lateral (axillary) border
7. Inferior angle

Answers to Figure 7.10 (a) and (b)

1. Head
2. Lesser tubercle
3. Anatomical neck
4. Intertubercular sulcus (bicipital groove)
5. Surgical neck
6. Body
7. Coronoid fossa
8. Olecranon fossa
9. Medial epicondyle
10. Trochlea
11. Capitulum
12. Lateral epicondyle
13. Radial fossa
14. Deltoid tuberosity
15. Greater tubercle

Answers to Figure 7.10 (c) through (e)

1. Coronoid process of ulna
2. Radial tuberosity
3. Head of ulna
4. Styloid process
5. Head
6. Styloid process of ulna
7. Olecranon process of ulna
8. Ulnar notch of radius
9. Trochlear (semilunar) notch
10. Radial notch of ulna

Answers to Figure 7.10 (f)

1. Distal phalanx
2. Middle phalanx
3. Proximal phalanx
4. Metacarpal
5. Capitate
6. Trapezoid
7. Trapezium
8. Scaphoid
9. Lunate
10. Triquetral
11. Pisiform
12. Hamate

Answers to Figure 7.11 (a) and (b)

1. Iliac crest
2. Iliac fossa
3. Anterior superior iliac spine
4. Anterior inferior iliac spine
5. Acetabulum
6. Superior ramus
7. Inferior ramus
8. Obturator foramen
9. Ramus
10. Ischial tuberosity
11. Lesser sciatic notch
12. Ischial spine
13. Greater sciatic notch
14. Posterior inferior iliac spine
15. Auricular surface
16. Posterior superior iliac spine

Answers to Figure 7.12 (a) and (b)

1. Head
2. Neck
3. Intertrochanteric line
4. Intertrochanteric crest
5. Lesser trochanter
6. Medial epicondyle
7. Medial condyle
8. Lateral epicondyle
9. Intercondylar fossa
10. Lateral condyle
11. Linea aspera
12. Patellar surface
13. Greater trochanter

Answers to Figure 7.12 (c) and (d)

1. Base
2. Apex
3. Articular facet for lateral femoral condyle
4. Articular facet for medial femoral condyle

Answers to Figure 7.12 (e)

1. Medial condyle
2. Intercondylar eminence
3. Lateral condyle
4. Tibial tuberosity
5. Medial malleolus
6. Fibular notch
7. Head of fibula
8. Lateral malleolus

Answers to Figure 7.12 (f)

1. Distal phalanx
2. Middle phalanx
3. Proximal phalanx
4. Metatarsal
5. Cuboid
6. Calcaneus
7. Talus
8. Navicular
9. Third (lateral) cuneiform
10. Second (intermediate) cuneiform
11. First (medial) cuneiform

Answers to Figure 7.13

1. Cranium
2. Face
3. Clavicle
4. Scapula
5. Sternum
6. Rib
7. Humerus
8. Ulna
9. Radius
10. Carpals
11. Phalanges of hand
12. Metacarpals
13. Femur
14. Patella
15. Tibia
16. Fibula
17. Tarsals
18. Metatarsals
19. Phalanges of foot
20. Hipbone
21. Vertebral column

4. Answers to Laboratory Report Questions:

Answers to Part 1. Multiple Choice

1. (c)
2. (d)
3. (a)
4. (c)
5. (b)
6. (b)
7. (d)
8. (c)
9. (c)
10. (a)

Answers to Part 2. Identification

11. Frontal bone
12. Temporal bone
13. Sphenoid bone
14. Ethmoid bone
15. Occipital bone
16. Mandible
17. Maxilla
18. Ethmoid bone
19. Sphenoid bone
20. Palatine bone
21. Sphenoid bone
22. Ethmoid bone
23. Temporal bone
24. Temporal bone
25. Temporal bone

Answers to part 3. Matching

26. N
27. K
28. C
29. R
30. Q
31. T
32. G
33. S
34. D
35. P
36. B
37. F
38. A
39. L

40. E
41. I
42. H
43. J
44. O
45. M

8
Articulations

1. Materials Needed:

Textbook of anatomy and physiology
Articulated skeleton
Charts, models, slide and preserved specimens of human joints
Articulated animal joints with ligaments
Sagittal section of an animal knee joint with ligaments
Rubber gloves
Laboratory coat

2. Suggested Audiovisual Materials

Videocassettes

Moving Parts (26 min; C; Sd; 1990; FHS)
The Human Body: What Can Go Wrong? (six filmstrips on video/cassettes/guide; EI)
Total Hip Arthroplasty — A New Approach (1997; EI)

Films: 16 mm

Human Skeleton (11 min; UWF)
One of Sixteen Million {arthritis} (17 min; C; Sd; KSU)

Films: 8 mm

Joint Movements: Introduction; Hinge Joints; Pivot Joints; Ball-and-Socket Joints; Saddle Joints; Gliding Joints (all EFL)

Transparencies: 35 mm

Pain in Rheumatology Medical Slide Series (188 slides; CARO)

Transparencies: overhead projection

Bone Joints (HSC)

Computer Software:

Flash: Bones and Joints (IBM; PLP)
Skeletal System (IBM; PLP)

3. Answers to Illustrations and/or Questions:

Answers to Figure 8.1

1. Synovial (joint) cavity
2. Fibrous capsule
3. Synovial membrane
4. Articular capsule
5. Periosteum
6. Articular cartilage

Answers to Figure 8.2

1. Hinge joint
2. Condyloid joint
3. Saddle joint
4. Pivot joint
5. Ball and socket joint
6. Planar joint

Answers to Figure 8.3 (a) through (t)

1. Flexion
2. Extension
3. Hypertension
4. Rotation
5. Abduction
6. Adduction
7. Plantar flexion
8. Protraction
9. Eversion
10. Flexion
11. Extension
12. Flexion
13. Flexion
14. Hyperextension
15. Circumduction
16. Depression
17. Lateral flexion
18. Extension
19. Lateral rotation
20. Medial rotation
21. Abduction
22. Extension
23. Abduction
24. Adduction
25. Rotation
26. Circumduction
27. Lateral rotation

Answers to Figure 8.4 (a) and (b)

1. tendon of quadriceps femoris muscle
2. patellar ligament
3. fibular (lateral) collateral ligament
4. posterior cruciate ligament
5. anterior cruciate ligament
6. medial meniscus
7. tibial (medial) collateral ligament
8. lateral meniscus

Answers to Figure 8.4 (c)

1. Posterior cruciate ligament
2. Anterior cruciate ligament
3. Patellar ligament

Answers to Figure 8.4 (d) and (e)

1. Gastrocnemius muscle
2. Oblique popliteal ligament
3. Anterior cruciate ligament
4. Fibular (lateral) collateral ligament
5. Lateral meniscus
6. Posterior cruciate ligament
7. Medial meniscus
8. Tibial (medial) collateral ligament

Answers to Figure 8.4 (f)

1. Tendon of quadriceps femoris muscle
2. Patellar ligament
3. Lateral meniscus
4. Gastrocnemius muscle

F. Answers to Table 8.1 ***Types of Joints According to Articular Components, Structural and Functional Classification, and Movements***

Joint	Articular Component	Classification	Movements
Axial Skeleton			
Suture	Found between skull bones	*Structural*: fibrous *Functional:* synarthrosis	None
Temporo-mandibular (TMJ)	Between condylar process of mandible and mandibular fossa and articular tubercle of temporal bone	*Structural:* synovial (combined hinge and planar joint) *Functional:* diathrosis	Depression, elevation, protraction, retraction, lateral displacement, and slight rotation of mandible
Atlanto-occipital	Between superior articular facets of atlas and occipital condyles of occipital bone	*Structural:* synovial (condyloid) *Functional:* diathrosis	Flexion and extension of head and slight lateral flexion of head to either side
Atlanto-axial	(1) Between dens of axis and (2) between lateral masses of atlas and axis.	*Structural:* synovial (pivot) between dens and anterior arch and synovial (planar) between lateral masses. *Functional:* diathrosis	Rotation of head
Intervertebral	(1) Between vertebral bodies and (2) between vertebral arches	*Structural:* cartilaginous (symphysis) between vertebral bodies and synovial (planar) between vertebral arches	Flexion, extension, lateral flexion, and rotation of vertebral column
Vertebrocostal	(1) Between facets of heads of ribs and facets of bodies of adjacent vertebrae and intervertebral discs between them and (2) between articular part of tubercles of ribs and facets of transverse processes of thoracic vertebrae	*Structural:* synovial (planar) *Functional:* diathrosis	Slight gliding

Table 8.1 (Continued)

Sternocostal	Between sternum and first seven pairs of ribs	*Structural:* cartilaginous (synchondrosis) between sternum and first pair of ribs and synovial (planar) between sternum and second through seventh pairs of ribs	None between sternum and first pair of ribs; slight gliding between sternum and second through seventh pairs of ribs
Lumbrosacral	(1) Between body of fifth lumbar vertebra and bases of sacrum and (2) between inferior articular facets of fifth lumbar vertebra and superior articular facets of first vertebra of sacrum	*Structural:* cartilaginous (symphysis) between body and base and synovial (planar) between articular facets *Functional:* amphiarthrosis between body and base and diathrosis between articular facets	Flexion, extension, lateral flexion, and rotation of vertebral column
Pectoral Girdles and Upper Limbs			
Sterno-clavicular	Between sternal end of clavicle, manubrium of sternum, and first costal cartilage	*Structural:* synovial (planar and pivot) *Functional:* diathrosis	Gliding with limited movements in nearly every direction
Acromio-clavicular	Between acromion of scapula and acromial end of clavicle	*Structural:* synovial (planar) *Functional:* diathrosis	Gliding and rotation of scapula on clavicle
Shoulder (glenohumeral)	Between head of humerus and glenoid cavity of scapula	*Structural:* synovial (ball-and-socket) *Functional:* diathrosis	Flexion, extension, hyperextension, abduction, adduction, medial and lateral rotation, and circumduction of arm
Elbow	Between trochlea of humerus, trochlear notch of ulna, and head of radius	*Structural:* synovial (hinge) *Functional:* diathrosis	Flexion and extension of forearm
Radioulnar	Proximal radioulnar joint between head of radius and radial notch of ulna; distal radioulnar joint between ulnar notch of radius and head of ulna	*Structural:* synovial (pivot) *Functional:* diathrosis	Rotation of forearm

Table 8.1 (continued)

Wrist (radiocarpal)	Between distal end of radius and scaphoid, lunate, and triquetrum of carpus	*Structural:* synovial (condyloid) *Functional:* diathrosis	Flexion, extension, abduction, adduction, and circumduction of wrist
Intercarpal	Between proximal row of carpal bones, distal row of carpal bones, and between both rows of carpal bones (midcarpal joints)	*Structural:* synovial (planar), except for hamate, scaphoid, and lunate (midcarpal) joint, which is synovial (saddle) *Functional:* diathrosis	Gliding plus flexion and abduction at midcarpal joints
Carpo-metacarpal	Carpometacarpal joint of thumb between trapezium of carpus and first metacarpal. Carpometacarpal joints of remaining digits formed between carpus and second through fifth metacarpals	*Structural:* synovial (saddle) at thumb and synovial (planar) at remaining digits *Functional:* diathrosis	Flexion, extension, abduction, adduction, and circumduction at thumb and gliding at remaining digits
Metacarpo-phalangeal	Between heads of metacarpals and bases of proximal phalanges	*Structural:* synovial (condyloid) *Functional:* diathrosis	Flexion, extension, abduction, adduction, and circumduction of phalanges
Inter-phalangeal	Between heads of phalanges and bases of more distal phalanges	*Structural:* synovial (hinge) *Functional:* diathrosis	Flexion and extension of phalanges

Table 8.1 (continued)

Pelvic Girdle and Lower Limbs

Sacroiliac	Between auricular surfaces of sacrum and ilia of hip bones	*Structural:* synovial (planar) *Functional:* diathrosis	Slight gliding (even more so during pregnancy)
Pubic symphysis	Between anterior surfaces of hip bones	*Structural:* cartilaginous (symphysis) *Functional:* amphiarthrosis	Slight movements (even more so during pregnancy)
Hip (coxal)	Between head of femur and acetabulum of hip bones	*Structural:* synovial (ball-and-socket) *Functional:* diathrosis	Flexion, extension, abduction, adduction, circumduction and rotation of thigh.
Knee (tibio-femoral)	Formed by (1) lateral tibiofemoral joint between lateral condyle of femur, lateral meniscus, and lateral condyle of tibia; (12) intermediate patellofemoral joint between patella and patellar surface of femur; (3) medial tibiofemoral joint between medial condyle of femur, medial meniscus, and medial condyle of tibia	*Structural:* synovial (hinge) at lateral and medial tibiofemoral joints; partly synovial (hinge) and synovial (planar) at patellofemoral joint *Functional:* diathrosis	Flexion, extension, slight medial rotation and lateral rotation of leg in flexed position
Tibiofibular	Proximal tibiofibular joint between lateral condyle of tibia and head of fibula; distal tibiofibular joint between distal end of fibula and fibular notch of tibia	*Structural:* synovial (planar) at proximal joint and fibrous (syndesmosis) at distal end *Functional:* diathrosis at proximal joint and amphiarthrosis at distal joint	Slight gliding at proximal joint and slight rotation of fibula during dorsiflexion of foot
Ankle (talocrural)	(1) Between distal end of tibia and its medial malleolus and talus and (2) between lateral malleolus of fibula and talus	*Structural:* synovial (hinge) *Functional:* diathrosis	Dorsiflexion and plantar flexion of foot

Table 8.1 (continued)

Intertarsal	Subtalar joint between talus and calcaneus of tarsus; talo-calcaneo-navicular joint between talus and calcaneus and navicular of tarsus; cal-caneocuboid joint between calcaneus and cuboid of tarsus	*Structural:* synovial (planar) at subtalar and calcaneocuboid joints and synovial at talocalcaneonavicular joint *Functional:* diathrosis	Inversion and eversion of foot
Tarso-metatarsal	Between three cuneiforms of tarsus and bases of five metatarsal bones	*Structural:* synovial (planar) *Functional:* diathrosis	Slight gliding
Metatarso-phalangeal	Between heads of metatarsals and bases of proximal phalanges	*Structural:* synovial (hinge) *Functional:* diathrosis	Flexion, extension, abduction, adduction, and circumduction of phalanges
Inter-phalangeal	Between heads of phalanges and bases of more distal phalanges	*Structural:* synovial (hinge) *Functional:* diathrosis	Flexion and extension of phalanges

4. Answers to Laboratory Report Questions:

Answers to Part 1. Multiple Choice

1. (b)
2. (c)
3. (d)
4. (b)
5. (a)
6. (b)
7. (d)
8. (d)
9. (b)
10. (a)

Answers to Part 2. Completion

11. Articular
12. Articular
13. Articular discs (menisci)
14. Bursae
15. Oblique popliteal
16. Lateral flexion
17. Laterally
18. Biaxial

Answers to Part 3. Matching

19. J
20. F
21. A
22. H
23. B
24. D
25. I
26. G
27. C
28. E
29. K

9
Muscle Tissue

1. Materials Needed:

Textbook of anatomy and physiology
Compound microscope
Lens paper
Microscope slides and cover glass
Prepared slides of:
- Skeletal muscle in longitudinal and transverse sections
- Smooth muscle in longitudinal and transverse sections
- Cardiac muscle in longitudinal and transverse sections
- Skeletal muscle showing nerve endings

Electron micrographs of skeletal muscle tissue
Models. charts. and slides of muscle tissue
Living frogs
Polygraph and accessory apparatus
Stimulator and stimulating electrodes
Skin electrodes (or ECG electrodes)
Electrode jelly
High-gain coupler (amplifier)
Tennis ball
Dishwashing pad
Dissecting instruments and tray
Rubber gloves
Laboratory coat
Ring stands and clamps
Time maker
Filter paper
Ringer's solution (to 100 mL of distilled water. add 0.65g of NaCl, 0.0 148 KCl, 0.0 12g $CaCl_2$, 0.02g $NaHCO_3$ and 0.00 1 g NaH_2PO_1)
100g weight
Glycerinated muscle preparations and solutions (available from Carolina Biological Supply Company)
Medicine Dropper
Millimeter ruler
Tracing needles
Ice

2. Suggested Audiovisual Materials

Videocassettes

Anabolic Steroids: Quest for Superman (31 min; 1991; HRM)
Bulking Up: The Dangers of Steroids (23 min; C; Sd; 1990; KSU)
Moving Parts (26 min; C; Sd; 1990; FHS)
Muscle Power (26 min; C; Sd; 1990; FHS)
Muscle Power (26 min; C; Sd; FHS)
Muscles and Exercise (29 min; C; Sd; 1990; TM)
Steroid Alert (20 min; C; Sd; 1990; KSU)

Films: 16 mm

Muscle Power (26 min; C; Sd; FHS)

Films: 8 mm

Muscle Contraction (Si; H&R)

Transparencies: 35 mm

Histology of the Skeletomuscular System (El)
Muscle Contraction (20 slides/guide; EI)
Muscle Contraction Set (20 slides: CARO)
Muscular System (Slides 32-46; McG)
Muscular System and Its Function (20 slides; EI)
Muscular Tissue Set (20 slides; CARO)
Striated Muscle Tissue Set (11 slides; CARO)
Systems of the Human Body: The Muscular System and Its Functional Set (20 slides: CARO)
What is a Muscle? Set (53 slides; CARO)

Transparencies: overhead projection

Human Muscles, 1 & 2 (1 transparency each; CARO)
Muscle Contraction (20 transparencies; BM)
Skeleton and Muscles Set (6 transparencies with 10 overlays; CARO)
The Skeleton, Muscles, and Internal Organs (1 transparency with 3 overlays; CARO)
The Structure and Antagonism of Muscles (1 transparency; CARO)

Computer Software

Biochemistry of *Muscle* (IBM; EVCARO)
Dynamics Of the Human Muscular System (IBM; EI)
Exercises in Muscle Contraction (IBM; EI/CARO)
Graphic Human Anatomy and Physiology Tutor: Muscular System (IBM; PLP)
Mechanical Properties Of Active Muscle (IBM; QUEUE)
Muscular System (IBM; PLP)
Neuromuscular Concepts (IBM; QUEUE/PLP)
Skeletal Muscle Anatomy and Physiology (IBM; QUEUE/PLP)

3. Answers to Illustrations and/or Questions:

Answers to Figure 9.1 (a) and (b)

1. Striations
2. Sarcolemma
3. Endomysium
4. Nucleus

Answers to figure 9.2

1. Mitochondrion
2. Sarcoplasmic reticulum
3. Transverse (t) tubule
4. Triad
5. Sarcolemma
6. Myofibril

7. Thick filament
8. Thin filament
9. Z disc
10. A (anistropic) band
11. I (isotropic) band
12. Terminal cistern

Answers to figure 9.10

1. Sarcolemma
2. Intercalated disc
3. Nucleus
4. Striations

Answers to figure 9.11

1. Sarcolemma
2. Nucleus
3. Sarcoplasm
4. Muscle fiber

4. Answers to Laboratory Report Questions:

Answers to Part 1. Multiple Choice

1. (b)
2. (a)
3. (c)
4. (d)
5. (a)
6. (c)
7. (c)
8. (a)
9. (b)
10. (a)

Answers to Part 2. Completion

11. Excitability
12. Endomysium
13. Sarcomeres
14. Sarcolemma
15. H zone
16. Smooth muscle tissue
17. Extensibility
18. All-or-none principle
19. Myogram
20. Motor end plate
21. Calcium, myosin binding sites
22. ATP
23. Sarcoplasmic reticulum
24. Myosin
25. I
26. Motor unit
27. Synaptic vesicles
28. Intercalated discs
29. Gap junctions
30. Refractory period
31. Intermediate
32. Multiunit
33. Stress-relaxation response
34. Threshold

10
Skeletal Muscles

1. Materials Needed:

Textbook of anatomy and physiology
Torso with skeletal muscles
Charts and/or slides of skeletal muscles
Double-injected preserved cats
Dissecting instruments and trays
Rubber gloves
Laboratory coat
Biostat

2. Suggested Audiovisual Materials

Videocassettes

Anabolic Steroids: Quest for Superman (31 min; C; Sd; 1991; HRM)
Bulking Up: The Dangers of Steroids (23 min; C; Sd; 1990: KSU)
Dynamics of Fitness: The Body in Action (filmstrip on video; 1991; HRM)
Fitness and Conditioning: Benefits for a Lifetime (30 min: C: Sd; I991; HRM)
Muscle Power (26 min; C; Sd; 1990; FHS)
Steroid Alert (20 min; C; Sd; 1990; KSU)
The Human Body: What Can Go Wrong? (six filmstrips on video/cassettes/guide; EI)
What Can Go Wrong? (Muscular-Skeletal System) (40 min: C: PLP)

Films: 16 mm

Functional Anatomy of the Hand (40 min; TNF)
Muscle (30 min; C; Sd; CRM)
Muscle Power (26 min; C; Sd; FHS)
Muscles (30 min; C; Sd; 1961; McG/KSU)

Transparencies: 35 mm

Muscular System (Slides 3246)
Muscular System and Its Function (20 slides; EI)

Transparencies: overhead projection

Muscular System-Unit 4 (C, 13 transparencies; RJB)
Skeleton: Muscles: Back View: Skeleton: Muscles: Front View (both GAF)

Computer Software

Body Language: Muscular System (IBM, Macintosh; PLP)
Dynamics of the Human Muscular System (IBM; EI)
Flash: Skeletal Muscles (IBM; PLP)
Graphic Human Anatomy and Physiology Tutor: Muscular System (IBM; PLP)
Muscular System (IBM; PLP)
Skeletal Muscle Anatomy and Physiology (IBM: QUEUE/PLP)
Understanding Human Physiology: Exercise Physiology (IBM: PLP)

3. Answers to Illustrations and/or Questions:

Answers to Table 10.1 Arrangement of Fascicles

Arrangement	Description	Example
Parallel	Fascicles are parallel with longitudinal axis of muscle and terminate at either end in flat tendons	stylohyoid muscle
Fusiform	Fascicles are nearly parallel with longitudinal axis of muscle and terminate at flat tendons, but muscle tapers toward tendons where the diameter is less than that of the belly	digastric muscle
Pennate	Fascicles are short in relation to muscle length and the tendon extends nearly the the entire length of the muscle	
Unipennate	Fascicles are arranged on only one side of tendon	extensor digitorum longus muscle
Bipennate	Fascicles are arranged on both side of a centrally positioned tendon	rectus femoris muscle
Multipennate	Fascicles attach obliquely from many directions to several tendons	deltoid muscle
Circular	Fascicles are arranged in a circular pattern and enclose an orifice (opening)	orbicularis oris muscle
Triangular	Fascicles attached to a broad tendon converge to give the muscle a triangular appearance	pectoralis major muscle

Answers to Table 10.2 Characteristics Used for Naming Skeletal Muscles

Characteristic	Description	Example
Direction of muscle fibers	Direction of muscle fibers relative to the midline of the body **Rectus** means the fibers run parallel to the midline **Transverse** means the fibers run perpendicular to the midline **Oblique** means the fibers run diagonally to the midline	 rectus abdominis transversus abdominis external oblique
Location	Structure near which a muscle is found	Frontalis
Size	Relative size of the muscle **Maximus** means largest **Minimus** means smallest **Longus** means longest **Brevis** means short **Latissimus** means widest **Longissimus** means longest **Magnus** means large **Major** means larger **Minor** means smaller **Vastus** means great	 gluteus maximus gluteus minimus adductor longus peroneus brevis latissimus dorsi longissimus capitis adductor magnus pectoralis major pectoralis minor vastus lateralis
Number of origins	Number of tendons of origin **Biceps** means two origins **Triceps** means three origins **Quadriceps** means four origins	 biceps brachii triceps brachii quadriceps femoris
Shape	Relative shape of the muscle **Deltoid** means triangular **Trapezius** means trapezoid **Serratus** means saw-toothed **Rhomboideus** means rhomboid or diamond-shaped **Orbicularis** means circular **Pectinate** means comblike **Platys** means flat **Quadratus** means square **Gracilis** means slender	 deltoid trapezius serratus anterior rhomboideus major orbicularis oculi pectineus platysma quadratus femoris gracilis
Origin and insertion	Sites where muscle originates and inserts	sternocleidomastoid originates on sternum and clavicle and inserts on mastoid process of temporal bone

Answers to Table 10.2 Characteristics Used for Naming Skeletal Muscles (continued)

Action	Principal action of the muscle	
	Flexor: decreases the angle at a joint	flexor carpi radialis
	Extensor: increases the angle at a joint	extensor carpi ulnaris
	Abductor: moves a bone away from the midline	abductor pollicis brevis
	Adductor: moves a bone closer to the midline	adductor longus
	Levator: produces a superior movement	levator scapulae
	Depressor: produces an inferior movement	depressor labii inferioris
	Supinator: turns the palm superiorly or anteriorly	supinator
	Pronator: turns the palm inferiorly or posteriorly	pronator teres
	Sphincter: decreases the size of an opening	external anal sphincter
	Tensor: makes a body part more rigid	tensor fascia lata
	Rotator: Moves a bone around its longitudinal axis	obturator externus

Answers to Figure 10.1

1. Epimysium
2. Perimysium
3. Muscle fibers (cells)
4. Fascicle
5. Endomysium

Answers to Table 10.3 Muscles of Facial Expression

Muscle	Origin	Insertion	Action
Frontalis	Galea aponeurotica	Skin superior to supraorbital margin	Draws scalp anteriorly, elevates (raises) eyebrows, and wrinkles forehead horizontally
Occipitalis	Occipital bone and mastoid process of temporal bone	Galea aponeurotica	Draws scalp posteriorly
Orbicularis oris	Muscle fibers surrounding opening of mouth	Skin at corner of mouth	Closes and protrudes lips, compresses lips against teeth, and shapes lips during speech
Zygomaticus major	Zygomatic bone	Skin at angle of mouth and orbicularis oris	Draws angle of mouth superiorly and outward as in smiling or laughing
Levator labii superioris	Superior to infraorbital foramen of maxilla	Skin at angle of mouth and orbicularis oris	Elevates (raises) upper lip
Depressor labii inferioris	Mandible	Skin of lower lip	Depresses (lowers) lower lip
Bucinator	Alveolar processes of maxilla and mandible and pterygomandibular raphe (fibrous band extending form pterygoid process to the mandible)	Orbicularis oris	Presses cheeks against teeth and lips as in whistling, blowing, and sucking; draws corner of mouth laterally; assists in mastication (chewing) by keeping food between the teeth (and not between teeth and cheeks)
Mentalis	Mandible	Skin of chin	Elevates and protrudes lower lip and pulls skin of chin superiorly (as in pouting)

Answers to Table 10.3 (continued)

Muscle	Origin	Insertion	Action
Platysma	Fascia over deltoid and pectoralis major muscles	Mandible, muscles around angle of mouth, and skin of lower face	Draws outer part of lower lip inferiorly and backward as in pouting; depresses mandible
Risorius	Fascia over parotid (salivary) gland	Circular path around orbit	Draws angle of mouth laterally as in tenseness
Oribcularis oculi	Medial wall of orbit	Circular path around orbit	Closes eyes
Corrugator supercilli	Medial end of superciliary arch of frontal bone	Skin of eyebrows	Draws eyebrow inferiorly and wrinkles skin of forehead vertically, as in frowning
Levator palpebrae superioris	Roof of orbit (lesser wing of sphenoid bone)	Skin of upper eyelid	Elevates upper eyelid (opens eye)

Answers to Figure 10.2 (a) and (b)

1. Buccinator
2. Depressor labii inferioris
3. Mentalis
4. Platysma
5. Orbicularis oris
6. Risorius
7. Zygomaticus major
8. Levator labii superioris
9. Orbicularis oculi
10. Frontalis

Answers to Figure 10.2 (c)

1. Frontalis
2. Orbicularis oculi
3. Levator labii superioris
4. Zygomaticus major
5. Buccinator
6. Orbicularis oris
7. Risorius
8. Platysma
9. Occipitalis

Answers to Table 10.4 Muscles That Move the Mandible (Lower Jaw)

Muscle	Origin	Insertion	Action
Masseter	Maxilla and zygomatic arch	Angle and ramus of mandible	Elevates mandible as in closing the mouth and retracts (draws back) mandible
Temporalis	Temporal and frontal bones	Coronoid process and ramus of mandible	Elevates and retracts mandible
Medial pterygoid	Medial surface of lateral pterygoid process of sphenoid and maxilla	Angle and ramus of mandible	Elevates and protracts (protrudes) mandible and moves mandible from side to side
Lateral Pterygoid	Greater wing and lateral surface of lateral pterygoid process of sphenoid	Condyle of mandible and temporomandibular joint (TMJ)	Protracts mandible, depresses mandible as in opening mouth, and moves mandible from side to side

Answers to Figure 10.3

1. Temporalis
2. Masseter
3. Lateral pterygoid
4. Medial pterygoid

Answers to Table 10.5 Muscles That Move the Eyeballs – The Extrinsic Muscles

Muscle	Origin	Insertion	Action
Superior rectus	Common tendinous ring (attached to bony orbit around optic foramen)	Superior and central part of eyeball	Moves eyeball superiorly (elevation), medially (adduction), and rotates it medially (clockwise)
Inferior rectus	Same as above	Inferior and central part of eyeball	Moves eyeball inferiorly (depression), medially (adduction), and rotates it laterally (counter-clockwise)
Lateral rectus	Same as above	Lateral side of eyeball	Moves eyeball laterally (abduction)
Medial rectus	Same as above	Medial side of eyeball	Moves eyeball medially (adduction)
Superior oblique	Sphenoid bone, superior and medial to the tendinous ring in the orbit	Eyeball between superior and lateral recti. The muscle inserts into the superior lateral surfaces of the eyeball via a tendon that passes through the trochlea	Moves eyeball inferiorly (depression), laterally (abduction), and rotates it medially (clockwise)
Inferior oblique	Maxilla in floor of orbit	Eyeball between inferior and lateral recti	Moves eyeball superiorly (elevation), laterally (abduction), and rotates it laterally (counter-clockwise)

Answers to Figure 10.4

1. Inferior oblique
2. Inferior rectus
3. Lateral rectus
4. Medial rectus
5. Superior rectus
6. Superior oblique

Answers to Table 10.6 Muscles That Move the Tongue – The Extrinsic Muscles

Muscle	Origin	Insertion	Action
Genioglossus	Mandible	Undersurface of tongue and hyoid bone	Depresses tongue and thrusts it anteriorly (protraction)
Styloglossus	Styloid process of temporal bone	Side and under surface of tongue	Elevates tongue and draws it posteriorly (retraction)
Palatoglossus	Anterior surface of soft palate	Side of tongue	Elevates posterior portion of tongue and draws soft palate down on tongue
Hyoglossus	Greater horn and body of hyoid bone	Side of tongue	Depresses tongue and draws down its sides

Answers to Figure 10.5

1. Genioglossus
2. Hyoglossus
3. Styloglossus
4. Palatoglossus

Answers to Table 10.7 Muscles of the Floor of the Oral Cavity (Mouth)

Muscle	Origin	Insertion	Action
Diagastric	Anterior belly from inner side of lower border of mandible; posterior belly from mastoid process of temporal bone	Body of hyoid bone via an intermediate tendon	Elevates hyoid bone and depresses mandible as in opening the mouth
Stylohyoid	Styloid process of temporal bone	Body of hyoid bone	Elevates hyoid bone and draws it posteriorly
Mylohyoid	Inner surface of mandible	Body of hyoid bone	Elevates hyoid bone and floor of mouth and depresses mandible
Geniohyoid	Inner surface of mandible	Body of hyoid bone	Elevates hyoid bone, draws hyoid bone and tongue anteriorly, and depresses mandible

Answers to Figure 10.6 (a) and (b)

1. Mylohyoid
2. Stylohyoid
3. Diagastric

Answers to Figure 10.6 (c) and (d)

1. Stylopharyngeus
2. Middle constrictor
3. Inferior constrictor
4. Palatopharyngeus

Answers to Table 10.8 Muscles of the Larynx (Voice Box)

Muscle	Origin	Insertion	Action
Extrinsic			
Omohyoid	Superior border of scapula and superior transverse ligament	Body of hyoid bone	Depresses hyoid bone
Sternohyoid	Medial end of clavicle and manubrium of sternum	Body of hyoid bone	Depresses hyoid bone
Sternothyroid	Manubrium of sternum	Thyroid cartilage of larynx	Depresses thyroid cartilage
Thyrohyoid	Thyroid cartilage of larynx	Greater horn of hyoid bone	Elevates thyroid cartilage and depresses hyoid bone
Stylopharyngeus	Medial side of base of styloid process	Lateral aspects of pharynx and thyroid cartilage	Elevates larynx and dilates pharynx to help bolus descend
Palatopharyngeus	Soft palate	Posterior border of thyroid cartilage and lateral and posterior wall of pharynx	Elevates larynx and pharynx and helps close nasopharynx during swallowing

Answers to Table 10.8 (continued)

Muscle	Origin	Insertion	Action
Intrinsic			
Cricothyroid	Anterior and lateral portion of cricoid cartilage of larynx	Anterior border of thyroid cartilage of larynx and posterior part of inferior border of thyroid cartilage of larynx	Elongates and places tension on vocal folds
Thyroarytenoid	Inferior portion of angle of thyroid cartilage of larynx and middle of cricothyroid ligament	Base and anterior surface of arytenoid cartilage of larynx	Shortens and relaxes vocal folds
Lateral cricoarytenoid	Superior border of cricoid cartilage of larynx	Anterior surface of arytenoid cartilage of larynx	Brings vocal folds together (adduction), thus closing the rim glottidis
Posterior cricoarytenoid	Posterior surface of cricoid cartilage of larynx	Posterior surface of arytenoid cartilage of larynx	Moves the vocal folds appart (abduction), thus opening the rima glottidis
Transverse and oblique arytenoid	Posterior surface and lateral border of one arytenoid cartilage of larynx	Corresponding parts of opposing arytenoid cartilage of larynx	The transverse arytenoid closes the posterior portion of the rima glottis; the oblique arytenoid regulates the size of the inlet of the larynx

Answers to Figure 10.7 (a) and (b)

1. Thyrohyoid
2. Sternothyroid
3. Omohyoid
4. Sternohyoid
5. Transverse and oblique arytenoid
6. Posterior cricoarytenoid
7. Thyroarytenoid
8. Lateral cricoarytenoid
9. Cricothyroid

Answers to Table 10.9 Muscles that Move the Head

Muscle	Origin	Insertion	Action
Sternocleidomastoid	Sternum and clavicle	Mastoid process of temporal bone	Acting together (bilaterally), flex cervical portion of vertebral column and head; acting singly (unilaterally) laterally flex and rotate head to side opposite contracting muscle
Semispinalis capitis	Transverse processes of first six or seven thoracic vertebrae and articular processes of fourth, fifth and sixth cervical vertebrae	Occipital bone	Acting together, extend head; acting singly, rotate head to side opposite contracting muscle
Splenius capitus	Ligamentum nuchae and spinous processes of seventh cervical vertebra and first three or four thoracic vertebrae	Occipital bone and mastoid process of temporal bone	Acting together, extend head; acting singly, laterally flex and rotate head to same side as contracting muscle
Longissimus capitus	Articular processes of last four cervical vertebrae and transverse processes of upper four thoracic vertebrae	Mastoid process of temporal bone	Acting together, extend head; acting singly, laterally flex and rotate head to same side as contracting muscle

Answers to Table 10.10 Muscles That Act On the Anterior Abdominal Wall

Muscle	Origin	Insertion	Action
Rectus abdominis	Pubic crest and pubic symphysis	Cartilage of fifth to seventh ribs and xiphoid process	Flexes vertebral column, especially lumbar portion, and compresses abdomen to aid in defecation, urination, forced expiration, and partirition (childbirth)
External oblique	Inferior eight ribs	Iliac crest and linea alba	Acting together, compress abdomen and flex vertebral column; acting singly, laterally flex vertebral column, especially lumbar portion and rotate vertebral column
Internal oblique	Iliac crest, inguinal ligament, and thoracolumbar fascia	Cartilage of last three or four ribs and linea alba	Acting together, compress abdomen and flex vertebral column; acting singly, laterally flex vertebral column, especially lumbar portion and rotate vertebral column
Transversus abdominis	Iliac crest, inguinal ligament, lumbar fascia, and cartilages of inferior six ribs	Xiphoid process, linea alba, and pubis	Compresses abdomen
Quadratus lumborum	Iliac crest and iliolumbar ligament	Inferior border of twelfth rib and transverse processes of first four lumbar vertebrae	Acting together , pull twelfth ribs inferiorly during forced expiration, fix twelfth ribs to prevent their elevation during deep inspiration, and help extend lumbar portion of vertebral column; acting singly, laterally flex vertebral column, especially lumbar portion

Answers to Figure 10.8

1. Internal oblique
2. Transversus abdominis
3. Rectus abdominis
4. External oblique

Answers to Table 10.11 Muscles Used in Ventilation (Breathing)

Muscle	Origin	Insertion	Action
Diaphragm	Xiphoid process, costal cartilages of last six ribs, and lumbar vertebrae	Central tendon	Forms floor of thoracic cavity; pulls central tendon inferiorly during inspiration and thus increases vertical length of thorax
External intercostals	Inferior border of rib above	Superior border of rib below	Elevate ribs during inspiration and thus increase lateral and anteroposterior dimensions of thorax
Internal intercostals	Superior border of rib below	Inferior border of rib above	Draw adjacent ribs together during forced expiration and thus decrease lateral and anteroposterior dimensions of thorax

Answers to Figure 10.9 (a) and (b)

1. External intercostals
2. Internal intercostals
3. Diaphragm

Answers to Table 10.12 Muscles of the Pelvic Floor

Muscle	Origin	Insertion	Action
Pubococcygeus	Pubis	Coccyx, urethra, anal canal, central tendon of perineum, and anococcygeal raphe (narrow fibrous band that extends from anus to coccyx)	Supports and maintains position of pelvic viscera; resists increase in intra-abdominal pressure during forced expiration, coughing, vomiting, urination, and defecation; constricts anus, urethra, and vagina; and supports fetal head during childbirth
Iliococcygeus	Ischial spine	Coccyx	As above
Coccygeus	Ischial spine	Inferior sacrum and superior coccyx	Supports and maintains position of pelvic viscera; resists increase in intra-abdominal pressure during forced expiration, coughing, vomiting, urinary, and defecation; and pulls coccyx anteriorly following defecation or childbirth

Answers to Figure 10.10

1. Superficial transverse perineus
2. Pubococcygeus
3. Iliococcygeus
4. External anal sphincter
5. Bulbospongiosus
6. Ischiocavernosus

Answers to Table 10.13 Muscles of the Perineum

Muscle	Origin	Insertion	Action
Superficial transverse perineus	Ischial tuberosity	Central tendon of perineum	Helps to stabilize central tendon of the perineum
Bulbospongiosus	Central tendon of perineum	Inferior fascia of the urogenital diaphragm, corpus spongiosum of penis and deep fascia on dorsum of penis in male, pubic arch and root of dorsum of clitoris in female	Helps expel last drops of urine during micturation (urination), helps propel semen along urethra, and assists in erection of the penis in male; constricts vaginal orifice and assists in erection of clitoris in female
Ischiocavernosus	Ischial tuberosity and ischia and pubic rami	Corpus cavernosum of penis in male and clitoris in female	Assists in maintaining erection of penis in male and clitoris in female
Deep transverse perineus	Ischial rami	Central tendon of perineum	Helps expel last drops of urine and semen in male and urine in female
Urethral sphincter	Ischial and pubic rami	Median raphe in male and vaginal wall in female	Helps expel last drops of urine and semen in male and urine in female
External anal sphincter	Anococcygeal raphe	Central tendon of perineum	Keeps anal canal and orifice closed

Answers to Table 10.14 Muscles That Move the Pectoral (Shoulder) Girdle

Muscle	Origin	Insertion	Action
Anterior Muscles			
Subclavius	First rib	Clavicle	Depresses and moves clavicle anteriorly and helps stabilize pectoral girdle
Pectoralis minor	Second through fifth, third through fifth, or second through fourth ribs	Coracoid process of scapula	Depresses and abducts scapula and rotates it downward; elevates third through fifth ribs during forced inspiration when scapula is fixed
Serratus anterior	Superior eight or nine ribs	Vertebral border and inferior angle of scapula	Abducts scapula and rotates it upward; elevates ribs when scapula is fixed; known as "boxer's muscle."
Posterior Muscles			
Trapezius	Occipital bone, ligamentum nuchae, and spines of seventh cervical and all thoracic vertebrae	Clavicle and acromion and spine of scapula	Superior fibers elevate scapula and can help extend head; middle fibers adduct scapula; inferior fibers depress scapula; superior and inferior fibers together rotate scapula upward; stabilizes scapula
Levator scapulae	Superior four or five cervical vertebrae	Superior vertebral border of scapula	Elevates scapula and rotates it downward
Rhomboideus major	Spines of second to fifth thoracic vertebrae	Vertebral border of scapula inferior to spine	Elevates and adducts scapula and rotates it downward; stabilizes scapula
Rhomboideus minor	Spines of seventh cervical and first thoracic vertebrae	Vertebral border of scapula superior to spine	Elevates and adducts scapula and rotates it downward; stabilizes scapula

Answers to Figure 10.11 (a) and (b)

1. Pectoralis minor
2. Serratus anterior
3. Pectoralis major
4. Sternocleidomastoid
5. Subclavius

Answers to Figure 10.11 (c) and (d)

1. Levator scapulae
2. Rhomboideus minor
3. Rhomboideus major
4. Trapezius

Answers to Table 10.15 Muscles that Move the Humerus (Arm)

Muscle	Origin	Insertion	Action
Axial Muscles			
Pectoralis major	Clavicle (clavicular head), sternum, and costal cartilages of second to sixth ribs (sometimes first to seventh ribs) (sternocostal head)	Greater tubercle and intertubercular sulcus of humerus	As a whole, adducts and medially rotates arm at shoulder joint; clavicular head alone flexes arm, and sternocostal head alone extends arm at shoulder joint
Latissimus dorsi	Spines of inferior six thoracic vertebrae, all lumbar vertebrae, crests of sacrum and ilium, inferior four ribs	Intertubercular sulcus of humerus	Extends, adducts, and medially rotates arm at shoulder joint; draws arm inferiorly and posteriorly
Scapular Muscles			
Deltoid	Arcomial extremity of clavicle (anterior fibers), acromion of scapula (lateral fibers), and spine of scapula (posterior fibers)	Deltoid tuberosity of humerus	Lateral fibers abduct arm at shoulder joint; anterior fibers flex and medially rotate arm at shoulder joint; posterior fibers extend and laterally rotate arm at shoulder joint
Subscapularis	Subscapular fossa of scapula	Lesser tubercle of humerus	Medially rotates arm at shoulder joint
Supraspinatus	Supraspinous fossa of scapula	Greater tubercle of humerus	Assists deltoid in abducting arm at shoulder joint

Answers to Table 10.15 Muscles that Move the Humerus (Arm) (continued)

Muscle	Origin	Insertion	Action
Scapular Muscles			
Infraspinatus	Infraspinous fossa of scapula	Greater tubercle of humerus	Laterally rotates and adducts arm at shoulder joint
Teres major	Inferior angle of scapula	Intertubercular sulcus of humerus	Extends arm at shoulder joint and assists in adduction and medial rotation of arm at shoulder joint
Teres minor	Inferior lateral border of scapula	Greater tubercle of humerus	Laterally rotates, extends, and adducts arm at shoulder joint
Coracobrachialis	Coracoid process of scapula	Middle of medial surface of shaft of humerus	Flexes and adducts arm at shoulder joint

Answers to Figure 10.12 (a) through (c)

1. Supraspinatus
2. Infraspinatus
3. Teres minor
4. Teres major
5. Latissimus dorsi
6. Deltoid
7. Subscapularis
8. Coracobrachialis

Answers to Table 10.16 Muscles That Move the Radius and Ulna (Forearm)

Muscle	Origin	Insertion	Action
Flexors			
Biceps brachii	Long head originates from tubercle above glenoid cavity; short head originates from coracoid process of scapula	Radial tuberosity and bicipital aponeurosis	Flexes forearm at elbow joint, supinates forearm at radioulnar joint, and flexes arm at shoulder joint
Brachialis	Distal anterior surface of humerus	Ulnar tuberosity and coronoid process of ulna	Flexes forearm at elbow joint
Brachioradialis	Medial and lateral borders of distal end of humerus	Superior to styloid process of radius	Flexes forearm at elbow joint and supinates and pronates forearm at radioulnar joints to neutral position

Answers to Table 10.16 Muscles That Move the Radius and Ulna (Forearm) (continued)

Muscle	Origin	Insertion	Action
Extensors			
Triceps brachii	Long head originates from a projection inferior to glenoid cavity of scapula; lateral head originates from lateral and posterior surfaces of humerus superior to radial groove; medial head originates from entire posterior surface of humerus inferior to groove for radial nerve	Olecranon of ulna	Extends forearm at elbow joint and extends arm at shoulder joint
Anconeus	Lateral epicondyle of humerus	Olecranon and superior portion of shaft of ulna	Extends forearm at elbow joint
Pronators			
Pronator teres	Medial epicondyle of humerus and coronoid process of ulna	Midlateral surface of radius	Pronates forearm at radioulnar joints and weakly flexes forearm at elbow joint
Pronator quadratus	Distal portion of shaft of ulna	Distal portion of shaft of radius	Pronates forearm at radioulnar joints
Supinator			
Supinator	Lateral epicondyle of humerus and ridge near radial notch of ulna	Lateral surface of proximal one-third of radius	Supinates at radioulnar joints

Answers to Figure 10.13 (a) and (b)

1. Triceps brachii
2. Brachioradialis
3. Brachialis
4. Biceps brachii
5. Pronator teres
6. Supinator

Answers to Table 10.17 Muscles That Move the Wrist, Hand and Digits

Muscle	Origin	Insertion	Action
Anterior Group (flexors)			
Superficial			
Flexor carpi radialis	Medial epicondyle of humerus	Second and third metacarpals	Flexes and abducts hand at wrist joint
Palmaris longus	Medial epicondyle of humerus	Flexor retinaculum and palmar aponeurosis (deep fascia in center of palm)	Weakly flexes hand at wrist joint
Flexor carpi ulnaris	Medial epicondyle of humerus and superior posterior border of ulna	Pisiform, hamate, and fifth metacarpal	Flexes and adducts hand (ulnar deviation) at wrist joint
Flexor digitorum superficialis	Medial epicondyle of humerus, coronoid process of ulna, and anterior oblique line of radius	Middle phalanges of each finger	Flexes middle phalanx of each finger at proximal interphalangeal joint, proximal phalanx of each finger at metacarpophalangeal joint, and hand at wrist joint
Deep			
Flexor digitorum profundus	Anterior medial surface of body of ulna	Bases of distal phalanges of each finger	Flexes distal and middle phalanx of each finger at interphalangeal joint, proximal phalanx of each finger at metacarpophalangeal joint, and hand at wrist joint
Flexor pollicis longus	Anterior surface of radius and interosseous membrane	Base of distal phalanx of thumb	Flexes distal phalanx of thumb at interphalangeal joint

Answers to Table 10.17 (continued)

Muscle	Origin	Insertion	Action
Posterior Group			
Superficial			
Extensor carpi radialis longus	Lateral supracondylar ridge of humerus	Second metacarpal	Extends and abducts hand at wrist joint
Extensor carpi radialis brevis	Lateral epicondyle of humerus	Third metacarpal	Extends and abducts hand at wrist joint
Extensor digitorum	Lateral epicondyle of humerus	Distal and middle phalanges of each finger	Extends distal and middle phalanges of each finger at interphalangeal joints, proximal phalanx of each finger at metacarpophalangeal joint, and hand at wrist joint
Extensor digiti minimi	Lateral epicondyle of humerus	Tendon of extensor digitorum on fifth phalanx	Extends proximal phalanx of little finger at metacarpophalangeal joint and hand at wrist joint
Extensor carpi ulnaris	Lateral epicondyle of humerus and posterior border of ulna	Fifth metacarpal	Extends and adducts hand at wrist joint
Deep			
Abductor pollicis longus	Posterior surface of middle of radius and ulna and interosseous membrane	Base of proximal phalanx of thumb	Abducts and extends thumb at metacarpophalangeal joint and abducts hand at wrist joint

Answers to Table 10.17 (continued)

Muscle	Origin	Insertion	Action
Extensor pollicis brevis	Posterior surface of middle of radius and interosseous membrane	Base of proximal phalanx of thumb	Extends proximal phalanx of thumb at metacarpophalangeal joint, first metacarpal of thumb at carpometacarpal joint, and hand at wrist joint
Extensor pollicis longus	Posterior surface of middle of ulna and interosseous membrane	Base of distal phalanx of thumb	Extends distal phalanx of thumb at interphalangeal joint, first metacarpal of thumb at carpometatarsal joint, and abducts hand at wrist joint
Extensor indicis	Posterior surface of ulna	Tendon of extensor digitorum of index finger	Extends distal and middle phalanx of index finger at interphalangeal joint, proximal phalanges of index finger at metacarpophalangeal joint, and hand at wrist joint

Answers to Figure 10.14 (a) and (b)

1. Flexor carpi radialis
2. Palmaris longus
3. Flexor carpi ulnaris
4. Flexor digitorum superficialis
5. Flexor digitorum profundus
6. Flexor pollicis longus

Answers to Figure 10.14 (c) and (d)

1. Extensor carpi radialis longus
2. Extensor digitorum
3. Extensor carpi radialis brevis
4. Abductor pollicis longus
5. Extensor pollicis brevis
6. Extensor pollicis longus
7. Extensor digiti minimi
8. Extensor carpi ulnaris
9. Extensor indicis
10. Flexor digitorum profundus
11. Flexor carpi ulnaris

Answers to Table 10.18 Intrinsic Muscles of the Hand

Muscle	Origin	Insertion	Action
Thenar Muscles			
Abductor pollicis bevis	Flexor retinaculum, scaphoid, and trapezium	Lateral side of proximal phalanx of thumb	Abducts thumb at carpometacarpal and metacarpophangeal joints
Opponens pollicis	Flexor retinaculum and trapezium	Lateral side of first metacarpal (thumb)	Moves thumb across palm to meet little finger (opposition) at the carpometacarpal joint
Flexor pollicis brevis	Flexor retinaculum, trapezium, capitate, and trapezoid	Lateral side of proximal phalanx of thumb	Flexes thumb at carpometacarpal and metacarpophalangeal joints
Adductor pollicis	Oblique head: capitate and second and third metacarpals; transverse head: third metacarpal	Medial side of proximal phalanx of thumb by a tendon containing a sesamoid bone	Adducts thumb at carpometacarpal and metacarpophalangeal joints
Hypothenar Muscles			
Abductor digiti minimi	Pisiform and tendon of flexor carpi ulnaris	Medial side of proximal phalanx of little finger	Abducts and flexes little finger at metacarpophangeal joints
Flexor digiti minimi brevis	Flexor retinaculum and hamate	Medial side of proximal phalanx of little finger	Flexes little finger at carpometacarpal and metacarpophalangeal joints
Opponens digiti minimi	Flexor retinaculum and hamate	Medial side of fifth metacarpal (little finger)	Moves little finger across palm to meet thumb (opposition) at the carpometacarpal joint
Intermediate (Midpalmar) Muscles			
Lumbricals	Lateral sides of tendons and flexor digitorum profundus of all four fingers	Lateral sides of tendons of extensor digitorum on proximal phalanges of all four fingers	Flexes fingers at metacarpophangeal joints and extend fingers at interphalangeal joints
Dorsal interossei	Adjacent sides of metacarpals	Proximal phalanx of all four fingers	Adduct fingers at metacarpophalangeal joints flex fingers at metacarpophalangeal joints and extend fingers at interphalangeal joints
Palmar interossei	Sides of shafts of metacarpals of all digits (except the middle one)	Sides of bases of proximal phalanges of all digits (except the middle one)	Adduct fingers at metacarpophalangeal joints flex fingers at metacarpophangeal joints

Answers to Figure 10.15 (a) and (b)

1. Abductor digiti minim
2. Opponens digiti minimi
3. Flexor digiti minimi brevis
4. Lumbricals
5. Abductor pollicis
6. Flexor pollicis brevis
7. Abductor pollicis brevis
8. Opponens pollicis
9. Dorsal interossei
10. Palmar interossei

Answers to Table 10.19 Muscles That Move the Vertebral Column (Backbone)

Muscle	Origin	Insertion	Action
Splenius Muscles			
Splenius capitis	Ligamentum nuchae and spinous processes of seventh cervical and first three or four thoracic vertebrae	Occipital bone and mastoid process of temporal bone	Acting together (bilaterally), extend head; acting singly (unilaterally), laterally flex and rotate head to same side as contracting muscle
Splenius cervicis	Spinous processes of third through sixth thoracic vertebrae	Transverse processes of first two or four cervical vertebrae	Acting together, extend head; acting singly, laterally flex and rotate head to same side as contracting muscle
Erector Spinae			
Iliocostalis Group (lateral)			
Iliocostalis cervicis	Superior six ribs	Transverse processes of fourth to sixth cervical vertebrae	Acting together, muscles of each region (cervical, thoracic, and lumbar) extend and maintain erect posture of vertebral column of their respective regions; acting singly, laterally flex vertebral column of their respective regions
Iliocostalis thoracis	Inferior six ribs	Superior six ribs	
Iliocostalis lumborum	Iliac crest	Inferior six ribs	

Answers to Table 10.19 Muscles That Move the Vertebral Column (Backbone)

Muscle	Origin	Insertion	Action
Longissimus Group (Intermediate)			
Longissimus capitis	Transverse processes of superior four thoracic vertebrae and articular processes of inferior four cervical vertebrae	Mastoid process of temporal bone	Acting together, both longissimus capitis muscles extend head; acting singly, rotate head to same side as contracting muscle.
Longissimus cervicis	Transverse processes of fourth and fifth thoracic vertebrae	Transverse processes of second to sixth cervical vertebrae	Acting together, longissimus cervicis and both longissimus thoracis muscles extend vertebral column of their respective regions; acting singly, laterally flex vertebral column of their respective regions
Longissimus thoracis	Transverse processes of lumbar vertebrae	Transverse processes of all thoracic and superior lumbar vertebrae and ninth and tenth ribs	
Spinalis Group (medial)			
Spinalis capitis	Arises with semispinalis capitis	Occipital bone	Acting together, muscles of each region (cervical, thoracic, and lumbar) extend vertebral column of their respective regions
Spinalis cervicis	Ligamentum nuchae and spinous processes of seventh cervical vertebra	Spinous process of axis	
Spinalis thoracis	Spinous processes of superior lumbar and inferior thoracic vertebrae	Spinous processes of superior thoracic vertebrae	

Answers to Table 10.19 Muscles That Move the Vertebral Column (Backbone) (continued)

Muscle	Origin	Insertion	Action
Transversospinalis Muscles			
Semispinalis capitis	Transverse processes of first six or seven thoracic vertebrae and seventh cervical vertebra,and articular processes of fourth, fifth, and sixth cervical vertebrae	Occipital bone	Acting together, extend head; acting singly, rotate head to side opposite contracting muscle
Semispinalis cervicis	Transverse processes of superior five or six thoracic vertebrae	Spinous processes of first to fifth cervical vertebrae	Acting together, both semispinalis cervicis and both semispinalis thoracis muscles extend vertebral column of their respective regions; acting singly, rotate head to side opposite contracting muscle
Semispinalis thoracis	Transverse processes of sixth to tenth thoracic vertebrae	Spinous processes of superior four thoracic and last two cervical vertebrae	
Multifidus	Sacrum, ilium, transverse processes of lumbar, thoracic, and inferior four cervical vertebrae	Spinous process of a more superior vertebra	Acting together, extend vertebral column; acting singly, laterally flex vertebral column and rotate head to side opposite contracting muscle
Rotatores	Transverse processes of all vertebrae	Spinous process of vertebra superior to the one of origin	Acting together, extend vertebral column; acting singly, rotate vertebral column to side opposite contracting muscle

Answers to Table 10.19 Muscles That Move the Vertebral Column (Backbone) (continued)

Muscle	Origin	Insertion	Action
Segmental Muscles			
Interspinales	Superior surface of all spinous processes	Inferior surface of spinous process of vertebra superior to the one of origin	Acting together, extend vertebral column; acting singly, stabilize vertebral column during movement
Intertransversarii	Transverse processes of all vertebrae	Transverse process of vertebra superior to the one of origin	Acting together, extend vertebral column; acting singly, laterally flex vertebral column and stabilize it during movements
Scalene Muscles			
Anterior scalene	Transverse processes of third through sixth cervical vertebrae	First rib	Acting together, both anterior scalene and middle scalene muscles flex head and elevate first ribs during deep inspiration; acting singly, laterally flex head and rotate head to side opposite contracting muscle
Middle scalene	Transverse processes of inferior six cervical vertebrae	First rib	
Posterior scalene	Transverse processes of fourth through sixth cervical vertebrae	Second rib	Acting together, flex head and elevate second ribs during deep inspiration; acting singly, laterally flex head and rotate head to side opposite contracting muscle

Answers to Figure 10.16 (a)

1. Spinalis capitis
2. Semispinalis capitis
3. Longissimus capitis
4. Semispinalis cervicis
5. Iliocostalis cervicis
6. Longissimus cervicis
7. Spinalis thoracis
8. Iliocostalis thoracis
9. Longissimus thoracis
10. Iliocostalis lumborum
11. Multifidus
12. Semispinalis thoracis
13. Spinalis cervicis
14. Splenius cervicis
15. Splenius capitis

Answers to Figure 10.16 (b)

1. Intertransversarii
2. Interspinales
3. Rotatores

Answers to Figure 10.16 (c)

1. Anterior scalene
2. Middle scalene
3. Posterior scalene

Answers to Table 10.20 Muscles that Move the Femur (Thigh)

Muscle	Origin	Insertion	Action
Psoas major	Transverse processes and bodies of lumbar vertebrae	With iliacus into lesser trochanter of femur	Both psoas major and iliacus muscles acting together flex thigh at hip joint, rotate thigh laterally, and flex trunk on the hip as in sitting up from the supine position
Iliacus	Iliac fossa	With psoas major into lesser trochanter of femur	
Gluteus maximus	Iliac crest, sacrum, coccyx, and aponeurosis of sacrospinalis	Iliotibial tract of fascia lata and gluteal tuberosity of femur	Extends thigh at hip joint and medially rotates thigh
Gluteus medius	Ilium	Greater trochanter of femur	Abducts thigh at hip joint and medially rotates thigh
Gluteus minimus	Ilium	Greater trochanter of femur	Abducts thigh at hip joint and medially rotates thigh
Tensor fasciae latae	Iliac crest	Tibia by way of iliotibial tract	Flexes and abducts thigh at hip joint

Answers to Table 10.20 (continued)

Muscle	Origin	Insertion	Action
Piriformis	Anterior sacrum	Superior border of greater trochanter of femur	Laterally rotates and abducts thigh at hip joint
Obturator internus	Inner surface of obturator foramen, pubis, and ischium	Greater trochanter of femur	Laterally rotates and abducts thigh at hip joint
Obturator externus	Outer surface of obturator membrane	Trochanteric fossa of femur	Laterally rotates and abducts thigh at hip joint
Superior gemellus	Ischial spine	Greater trochanter of femur	Laterally rotates and abducts thigh at hip joint
Inferior gemellus	Ischial tuberosity	Greater trochanter of femur	Laterally rotates and abducts thigh at hip joint
Quadratus femoris	Ischial tuberosity	Quadrate tubercle on posterior femur	Laterally rotates and adducts thigh at hip joint
Adductor longus	Pubic crest and pubic symphysis	Linea aspera of femur	Adducts and flexes thigh at hip joint and medially rotates thigh
Adductor brevis	Inferior ramus of pubis	Superior half of linea aspera	Adducts and flexes thigh at hip joint and medially rotates thigh
Adductor magnus	Inferior ramus of pubis and ischium to ischial tuberosity	Linea aspera of femur	Adducts and medially rotates thigh at hip joint; anterior part flexes thigh at hip joint and posterior part extends thigh at hip joint.
Pectineus	Superior pubic ramus	Pectineal line of femur between lesser trochanter and linea aspera	Flexes and adducts thigh at hip joint

Answers to Figure 10.17 (a) and (c)

1. Gluteus medius
2. Gluteus maximus
3. Gluteus minimus
4. Piriformis
5. Obturator internus
6. Adductor magnus
7. Adductor longus
8. Adductor brevis
9. Pectineus
10. Tensor fascia latae
11. Iliacus
12. Psoas major
13. Obturator externus
14. Superior gemellus
15. Inferior gemellus
16. Quadratus femoris

Answers to Table 10.21 Muscles that Act on the Tibia and Fibula (Leg)

Muscle	Origin	Insertion	Action
Medial (Adductor) Compartment			
Adductor longus	Pubic crest and pubic symphysis	Linea aspera of femur	Adducts and flexes thigh at hip joint and medially rotates thigh
Adductor brevis	Inferior ramus of pubis	Superior half of linea aspera	Adducts and flexes thigh at hip joint and medially rotates thigh
Adductor magnus	Inferior ramus of pubis and ischium to ischial tuberosity	Linea aspera of femur	Adducts and medially rotates thigh at hip joint; anterior part flexes thigh at hip joint and posterior part extends thigh at hip joint.
Gracilis	Pubic symphysis and pubic arch	Medial surface of body of tibia	Adducts thigh at hip joint, laterally rotates thigh, and flexes leg at knee joint
Anterior (Extensor) Compartment			
Quadraceps femoris			
Rectus femoris	Anterior inferior iliac spine	Patella via quadriceps tendon and then tibial tuberosity via patellar ligament	All four heads extend leg at knee joint; rectus femoris muscle acting alone also flexes thigh at hip joint
Vastus lateralis	Greater trochanter and linea aspera of femur		
Vastus medialis	Linea aspera of femur		
Vastus intermedius	Anterior and lateral surfaces of body of femur		
Sartorius	Anterior superior iliac spine of ilium	Medial surface of body of tibia	Flexes leg at knee joint, flexes thigh at hip joint, and laterally rotates thigh, thus crossing leg

Answers to Table 10.21 Muscles that Act on the Tibia and Fibula (Leg) (continued)

Muscle	Origin	Insertion	Action
Posterior (Flexor) Compartment			
Hamstrings (A collective designation for three separate muscles)			
Biceps femoris	Long head arises from ischial tuberosity; short head arises from linea aspera of femur	Head of fibula and lateral condyle of tibia	Flexes leg at knee joint and extends thigh at hip joint
Semitendinosus	Ischial tuberosity	Proximal part of medial surface of body of tibia	Flexes leg at knee joint and extends thigh at hip joint
Semimembranosus	Ischial tuberosity	Medial condyle of tibia	Flexes leg at knee joint and extends thigh at hip joint

Answers to Figure 10.18 (a) and (b)

1. Semitendinosus
2. Biceps femoris
3. Semimembranosus
4. Gracilis
5. Sartorius
6. Vastus medialis
7. Vastus lateralis
8. Vastus intermedius
9. Rectus femoris

Answers to Table 10.22 Muscles that Move the Foot and Toes

Muscle	Origin	Insertion	Action
Anterior Compartment			
Tibialis anterior	Lateral condyle and body of tibia and interosseous membrane	First metatarsal and first (medial) cuneiform	Dorsiflexes foot at ankle joint and inverts foot at intertarsal joints
Extensor hallucis longus	Anterior surface of fibula and interosseous membrane	Distal phalanx of great toe	Dorsiflexes foot at ankle joint, inverts foot at intertarsal joints, and extends proximal phalanx of great toe at metatarsophalangeal joint
Extensor digitorum longus	Lateral condyle of tibia, anterior surface of fibula, and interosseous membrane	Middle and distal phalanges of toes two through five	Dorsiflexes foot at ankle joint, everts foot at intertarsal joints, and extends distal and middle phalanx of each toe and interphalangeal joint and proximal phalanx of each toe at meta-tarsophalangeal joint
Peroneus tertius	Distal third of fibula and interosseous membrane	Fifth metatarsal	Dorsiflexes foot at ankle joint and everts foot at intertarsal joints

Answers to Table 10.22 Muscles that Move the Foot and Toes (continued)

Muscle	Origin	Insertion	Action
Lateral (Peroneal) Compartment			
Peroneus longus	Head and body of fibula and lateral condyle of tibia	First metatarsal and first cuneiform	Plantar flexes foot at ankle joint and everts foo at intertarsal joints
Peroneus brevis	Body of fibula	Fifth metatarsal	Plantar flexes foot at ankle joint and everts foo at intertarsal joints
Posterior Compartment			
Superficial Layer			
Gastrocnemius	Lateral and medial condyles of femur and capsule of knee	Calcaneus by way of calcaneal (Achilles) tendon	Plantar flexes foot at ankle joint and flexes leg at knee joint
Soleus	Head of fibula and medial border of tibia	Calcaneus by way of calcaneal (Achilles) tendon	Plantar flexes foot at ankle joint
Plantaris	Femur superior to lateral condyle	Calcaneus by way of calcaneal (Achilles) tendon	Plantar flexes foot at ankle joint and flexes leg at knee joint
Deep Layer			
Popliteus	Lateral condyle of femur	Proximal tibia	Flexes leg at knee joint and medially rotates leg
Tibialis posterior	Tibia, fibula, and interosseous membrane	Second, third and fourth metatarsals; navicular; all three cuneiforms; and cuboid	Plantar flexes foot at ankle joint and inverts foot at intertarsal joints

Answers to Table 10.22 Muscles that Move the Foot and Toes (continued)

Muscle	Origin	Insertion	Action
Flexor hallucis longus	Inferior two-thirds of fibula	Distal phalanx of great toe	Plantar flexes foot at ankle joint and flexes distal phalanx of great toe at interphalangeal joint and proximal phalanx of great toe at metatarsophalangeal joint
Flexor digitorum longus	Posterior surface of tibia	Distal phalanges of toes two through five	Plantar flexes foot at ankle joint and flexes distal and middle phalanx of each toe at interphalangeal joint and proximal phalanx of each toe at metatarsophalangeal joint

Answers to Figure 10.19 (a) and (b)

1. Peroneus longus
2. Extensor digitorum longus
3. Tibialis anterior
4. Peroneus brevis
5. Extensor hallucis longus
6. Peroneus tertius
7. Plantaris
8. Gastrocnemius
9. Soleus
10. Popliteus
11. Flexor digitorum longus
12. Tibialis posterior
13. Flexor hallucis longus

Answers to Table 10.23 Intrinsic Muscles of the Foot

Muscle	Origin	Insertion	Action
Dorsal Muscles			
Extensor digitorum brevis	Calcaneus and inferior extensor retinaculum	Tendons of extensor digitorum longus on toes two through four and proximal phalanx of great toe	Extends great toe at metatarsophalangeal joint and toes two through four at interphalangeal joints
Plantar Muscles			
First (Superficial) Layer			
Abductor hallucis	Calcaneus, plantar aponeurosis, and flexor retinaculum	Medial side of proximal phalanx of great toe with the tendon of the flexor hallucis brevis	Abducts and flexes great toe at metatarsophalangeal joint
Flexor digitorum brevis	Calcaneus and plantar aponeurosis	Sides of middle phalanx of toes two through five	Flexes toes two through five at proximal interphalangeal and metatarsaophalangeal joints
Abductor digiti minimi	Calcaneus and plantar aponeurosis	Lateral side of proximal phalanx of small toe with the tendon of the flexor digiti minimi brevis	Abducts and flexes small toe at metatarsophalangeal joint
Second Layer			
Quadratus plantae	Calcaneus	Tendon of flexor digitorum longus	Assists flexor digitorum longus to flex toes two through five at interphalangeal and metatarsophalangeal joints
Lumbricals	Tendons of flexor digitorum longus	Tendons of extensor digitorum longus on proximal phalanges of toes two to five	Extend toes two through five at interphalangeal joints and flex toes two through five at metatarsophalangeal joints

Answers to Table 10.23 Intrinsic Muscles of the Foot (continued)

Muscle	Origin	Insertion	Action
Third Layer			
Flexor hallucis brevis	Cuboid and third (lateral) cuneiform	Medial and lateral sides of proximal phalanx of great toe via a tendon containing a sesamoid bone	Flexes great toe at metatarsophalangeal joint
Adductor hallucis	Metatarsals two through four, ligaments of three through five metatarsophalangeal joints, and tendon of peroneus longus	Lateral side of proximal phalanx of great toe	Adducts and flexes great toe at metatarsophalangeal joint
Flexor digiti minimi brevis	Metatarsal five and tendon of peroneus longus	Lateral side of proximal phalanx of small toe	Flexes small toe at metatarsophalangeal joint
Fourth (Deep) Layer			
Dorsal interossei	Adjacent side of metatarsals	Proximal phalanges; both sides of toe two and lateral side of toes three through four	Abduct and flex toes two through four at metatarsophalangeal joints and extend toes at interphalangeal joints
Plantar interossei	Metatarsals three through five	Medial side of proximal phalanges of toes three through five	Adduct and flex proximal metatarsophalangeal joints and extend toes at interphalangeal joints

Answers to Figure 10.20 (a) and (b)

1. Lumbricals
2. Flexor hallucis brevis
3. Quadratus plantae
4. Flexor digitorum brevis
5. Abductor digiti minimi
6. Adductor hallucis
7. Flexor digiti minimi brevis
8. Abductor hallucis

Answers to Figure 10.20 (c) and (d)

1. Dorsal interossei
2. Plantar interossei

Answers to Figure 10.21 (a)

1. Frontalis
2. Orbicularis oculi
3. Orbicularis oris
4. Depressor labii inferioris
5. Platysma
6. Pectoralis major
7. Serratus anterior
8. External oblique
9. Rectus abdominis
10. Iliacus
11. Psoas major
12. Tensor fascia lata
13. Pectineus
14. Adductor longus
15. Sartorius
16. Gracilis
17. Gastrocnemius
18. Soleus
19. Peroneus longus
20. Tibialis anterior
21. Vastus medialis
22. Rectus femoris
23. Vastus lateralis
24. Flexor carpi ulnaris
25. Palmaris longus
26. Flexor carpi radialis
27. Pronator teres
28. Brachioradialis
29. Brachialis
30. Biceps brachii
31. Triceps brachii
32. Deltoid
33. Trapezius
34. Sternocleidomastoid
35. Mentalis
36. Zygomaticus major
37. Zygomaticus minor
38. Temporalis

Answers to Figure 10.21 (b)

1. Occipitalis
2. Semispinalis capitis
3. Sternocleidomastoid
4. Trapezius
5. Infraspinatus
6. Rhomboideus major
7. Deltoid
8. Teres minor
9. Teres major
10. Latissimus dorsi
11. External oblique
12. Gluteus medius
13. Gluteus maximus
14. Biceps femoris
15. Semitendinosus
16. Gracilis
17. Sartorius
18. Semimembranosus
19. Gastrocnemius
20. Soleus
21. Extensor carpi ulnaris
22. Extensor digitorum
23. Extensor carpi radialis longus
24. Brachioradialis
25. Triceps brachii

5. Answers to Laboratory Report Questions:

Answers to Part 1. Multiple Choice

1. c
2. d
3. a
4. b
5. c
6. d
7. a
8. d
9. c
10. a
11. c
12. b
13. d
14. b
15. a
16. d
17. a
18. d
19. a
20. c
21. b
22. a

Answers to Part 2. Matching

23. E
24. B
25. G
26. E, G
27. A, C
28. A, D
29. F
30. C, E
31. A
32. B

Answers to Part 3. Completion

33. buccinator
34. genioglossus
35. inferior rectus
36. sternocleidomastoid
37. rectus abdominis
38. subclavius
39. pectoralis major
40. triceps brachii
41. flexor carpi radialis
42. rectus femoris
43. infrahyoid (strap)
44. sternocleidomastoid
45. scapula
46. axial
47. rotator (musculocutaneous) cuff
48. supination
49. flexion
50. hamstrings
51. multipennate
52. flexion
53. inferiorly
54. suprahyoid
55. posterior cricoarytenoid
56. central tendon
57. pelvic diaphragm
58. urogenital
59. upward rotation
60. brachialis
61. palmaris longus
62. hypothenar
63. erector spinae (sacrospinalis)
64. pelvic girdle
65. quadriceps femoris
66. gastrocnemius
67. flexor

11
Surface Anatomy

1. Materials Needed:

Textbook of anatomy and physiology
Torso
Human Skeleton
Charts, models, slides, and photographs of surface anatomy features of the head, neck, trunk, and limbs (extremities)

2. Suggested Audiovisual Materials

Films: 16 mm

The Skeletal System (13 min; BW; EBEC)
The Human Skeleton (11 min; Sd; UWF)
Human Body: Muscular System(14 min; C; Sd; Cor)
Functional Anatomy of the Hand (40 min; TNF)
Muscles (28 min; C; Sd; McG)

Transparencies: 35 mm

Muscular System (Slides 32-46)
Muscular System and Its Functions (20 slides; EI)

Transparencies: overhead projection

Topographical Anatomy (slides 206 through 224; McG)
Skeletal System (HSC)
Skeletal System, Unit 2 (C; 27 transparencies; RJB)
Skeletal System (slides 6 through 31, McG)
Bone Joints (HSC)
Skeletal Muscles: Back View (GAF)
Skeletal Muscles: Front View (GAF)
Muscular System, Unit 4 (C; 13 transparencies; RJB)

Computer Software

Body Language: Muscular System (anatomy) (IBM, Macintosh; PLP)
Dynamics of the Human Musculature (IBM; EI)
Flash: Skeletal Muscles (IBM; PLP)
Graphic Human Anatomy and Physiology Tutor: Muscular System (IBM; PLP)
Muscular System (IBM; PLP)

3. Answers to Illustrations and/or Questions:

Answers to Figure 11.1

1. Zygomatic region
2. Orbital (ocular) region
3. Infraorbital region
4. Nasal region
5. Buccal region
6. Oral region
7. Mental region
8. Occipital region
9. Auricular region
10. Parietal region
11. Temporal region
12. Frontal region

Answers to Figure 11.2 (a) and (b)

1. Sagittal suture
2. Orbit
3. Nasal bone
4. Zygomatic arch
5. External auditory meatus
6. Temporomandibular joint
7. Ramus of mandible
8. Body of mandible
9. Mastoid process
10. External occipital protuberance
11. Superficial temporal artery
12. Coronal suture

Answers to Figure 11.3

1. Hyoid bone
2. External jugular vein
3. Thyroid cartilage
4. Cricoid cartilage
5. Sternocleidomastoid muscle
6. Trapezius muscle
7. Thyroid gland
8. Carotid pulse point

Answers to Figure 11.4

1. Submandibular triangle
2. Suprahyoid triangle
3. Carotid triangle
4. Muscular triangle
5. Anterior triangle
6. Supraclavicular triangle
7. Occipital triangle
8. Posterior triangle

Answers to Figure 11.5

1. Vertebra prominens
2. Trapezius muscle
3. Acromion of scapula
4. Infraspinatus muscle
5. Scapula
6. Posterior axillary fold
7. Teres major muscle
8. Triangle of auscultation
9. Spinous processes (spines)
10. Latissimus dorsi muscle
11. Erector spinae muscle

Answers to Figure 11.6

1. Clavicle
2. Suprasternal (jugular) notch of sternum
3. Manubrium of sternum
4. Sternal angle of sternum
5. Body of sternum
6. Xiphoid process of sternum
7. Costal margin
8. Serratus anterior muscle
9. Nipple
10. Anterior axillary fold
11. Pectoralis major muscle
12. Rib

Answers to Figure 11.7 (a)

1. Umbilicus
2. External oblique muscle
3. Rectus abdominis muscle
4. Linea alba
5. Tendinous intersection
6. McBurney's point
7. Linea semilunaris
8. Iliac crest
9. Anterior superior iliac crest

Answers to Figure 11.7 (b) and (c)

1. Umbilicus
2. Mons pubis
3. Pubic symphysis
4. Pubic tubercle
5. Inguinal ligament
6. Anterior superior iliac spine
7. Iliac crest
8. Supracristal line
9. Sacrum
10. Posterior superior iliac spine
11. Coccyx

Answers to Figure 11.8

1. Acromioclavicular joint
2. Greater tubercle of humerus
3. Deltoid muscle
4. Acromion of scapula

Answers to Figure 11.9 (a) through (c)

1. Olecranon of ulna
2. Bicipital aponeurosis
3. Biceps brachii muscle
4. Triceps brachii muscle
5. Groove for brachial artery
6. Cubital fossa
7. Medial epicondyle of humerus
8. Lateral epicondyle of humerus
9. Median cubital vein

Answers to Figure 11.10 (a) through (c)

1. Brachioradialis muscle
2. Tendon of flexor carpi radialis muscle
3. Site for palpation of radial artery
4. Pisiform bone
5. Tendon of flexor carpi ulnaris muscle
6. Tendon of palmaris longus muscle
7. Styloid process of ulna
8. "Anatomical snuffbox"
9. Tendon of extensor pollicis longus muscle
10. Tendon of extensor pollicis brevis muscle
11. Wrist creases
12. Styloid process of radius
13. Head of ulna
14. Tendon of flexor digitorum superficialis muscle

Answers to Figure 11.11 (a) through (d)

1. "Knuckles"
2. Thenar eminence
3. Hypothenar eminence
4. Digital flexion creases
5. Palmar flexion creases
6. Tendon of extensor digiti minimi muscle
7. Tendon of extensor digitorum muscle
8. Dorsal venous arch

Answers to Figure 11.12

1. Gluteus medius muscle
2. Gluteus maximus muscle
3. Gluteal (natal) cleft
4. Gluteal fold
5. Site of ischial tuberosity
6. Greater trochanter of femur

Answers to Figure 11.13 (a) through (c)

1. Adductor longus muscle
2. Sartorius muscle
3. Vastus medialis muscle
4. Vastus lateralis
5. Rectus femoris muscle
6. Femoral triangle
7. Patella
8. Medial condyle of femur
9. Medial condyle of tibia
10. Patellar ligament
11. Tibial tuberosity
12. Medial condyle of femur
13. Lateral condyle of femur
14. Site of semitendinosus and semimembranosus muscle
15. Tendon of semitendinosus muscle
16. Popliteal fossa
17. Tendon of biceps femoris muscle

Answers to Figure 11.14 (a) through (d)

1. Tibial tuberosity
2. Gastrocnemius muscle
3. Soleus muscle
4. Medial malleolus of tibia
5. Lateral malleolus of fibula muscle
6. Tibialis anterior muscle
7. Anterior border of tibia (shin)
8. Calcaneal (Achilles) tendon
9. Calcaneus
10. Tendons of extensor digitorum longus muscle
11. Tendon of extensor hallucis longus
12. Dorsal venous arch

4. Answers to Laboratory Report Questions:

Answers to Part 1. Multiple Choice

1. (c)
2. (d)
3. (b)
4. (d)
5. (a)
6. (a)
7. (c)
8. (d)
9. (b)
10. (d)
11. (c)
12. (a)
13. (b)
14. (b)
15. (c)

Answers to Part 2. Completion

16. Cricoid
17. Anterior
18. Jugular notch
19. Pectoralis major
20. Rectus abdominis
21. Deltoid
22. Cubital fossa
23. Extensor pollicis
24. "Knuckles"
25. Extensor digit minimi
26. Posterior superior iliac crest
27. Greater trochanter
28. Patellar ligament
29. Calcaneal (Achilles)
30. Dorsal venous arch
31. External jugular
32. Vertebral prominens
33. Sternal angle
34. Linea alba
35. Median cubital
36. Anterior
37. Posterior axillary fold
38. Auscultation
39. Xiphisternal

40. Supracristal
41. McBurney's point)
42. Linea semilunaris

Answers to Part 3. Multiple Choice

43. H
44. C
45. F
46. M
47. N
48. K
49. A
50. B
51. L
52. O
53. J
54. E
55. I
56. G
57. D

12
Nervous Tissue and Physiology

1. Materials Needed:

Textbook of anatomy and physiology
Compound microscope
Lens paper
Charts and models of neurons and neuroglia
Live frogs
Wire, one 4-in. piece per student
30% acetic acid solution
Filter paper cut into small squares
Stimulator and stimulating electrodes
Dissecting instruments and trays
Rubber gloves
Laboratory coat
Prepared slides of:
- Human spinal cord in longitudinal and transverse sections
- Ox spinal cord in longitudinal and transverse sections
- Nerve trunk in transverse section
- Protoplasmic astrocytes
- Fibrous astrocytes
- Oligodendrocytes
- Microglia
- Ependymal cells

2. Suggested Audiovisual Materials

Videocassettes

Drugs: How They Effect Body Chemistry (30 min; C; Sd; HRM)
Hard Facts about Drugs: Alcohol, Marijuana. Cocaine and Crack (22 min; C; Sd; 1991; GA)
Nerves at Work (26 min; C; Sd; 1990; FHS)
Neurobiology I: Excitatory Membranes (60 slides on video/cassette/guide; 1990; EI)
Neurobiology 11: Neural Function (75 slides on video/cassette/guide; 1990; EI)
Surviving Lifestyle Drugs (filmstrip on video; C; Sd; 199 I ; HRM)
The Addicted Brain (26 min; C; Sd; 1990; FHS)
The Danger Zone: Substance Abuse (17 min; C; Sd; 1990; PLP)
The Nervous System (48 min; C; Sd; GA)

Films: 16 mm

Fundamentals of the Nervous System (17 min; C; Sd; EBECYKSU)
Nerves at Work (26 min; C; Sd; 1990; FHS)

Films: 8 mm

Nerve Action: Reflex Arc (C; H&B)

Nerve Impulse, Part I: *Making the Preparation* (EC)
Nerve Impulse, Part II: *Performing the Demonstration* (EC)

Transparencies: 35 mm

Histology. of the Nervous System (EI)
Nervous System (Slides 173-205; McG)
Nervous System and Its Functions (20 slides; EI)
Nervous Systems (25 slides/guide; EI)
Nervous Tissue Set (20 slides; CARO)
Neurobiology I: Excitatory Membranes (60 slides/cassette/guide; EI)
Neurobiology II: Neural Function (75 slides/cassette/guide; EI)
Neurons and Impulse Propagation (PHM)
The Nerve Impulse (10 slides/guide; EI)
Visual Approaches to Histology: Nervous System (FAD)

Transparencies: overhead projection

The Neuron and Reflex Arc (K&E)
Nervous System: Stimulus, Response, Action (GAF)
The Central Nervous System— Conscious and Reflex Actions (transparency, 2 overlays. CARO)

Computer Software

Body Language: Nervous System [anatomy] (IBM, Macintosh; PLP)
Dynamics **of** *the Human Nervous System* (IBM; EI)
Flash: Neurons (Apple, IBM; PLP)
Graphic Human Anatomy and Physiology Tutor: Nervous System (IBM; PLP)
Nervous and Hormonal Systems (IBM, Macintosh; QUEUE)
Nervous System (IBM; PLP)
Support, Locomotion, and Behavior (IBM, Macintosh; QUEUE)

3. Answers to Illustrations and/or Questions:

Answers to Figure 12.1 (a) and (b)

1. Dendrites
2. Cell body
3. Axon hillock
4. Axon collateral
5. Initial segment
6. Axon
7. Myelin sheath
8. Neurofibril node (node of Ranvier)
9. Neurolemma (sheath of Schwann
10. Axolemma
11. Axon terminals
12. Synaptic end bulbs

Answers to Figure 12.2

1. Bipolar neuron
2. Multipolar neuron
3. Unipolar neuron

Answers to Figure 12.4

1. Diverging circuit
2. Converging circuit
3. Reverberating circuit
4. Parallel after-discharge circuit

Answers to Figure 12.5

1. Receptor
2. Sensory neuron
3. Integrating center
4. Motor neuron
5. Effector

5. Answers to Laboratory Report Questions:

Answers to Part 1. Multiple Choice

1. (b)
2. (c)
3. (d)
4. (a)
5. (b)
6. (b)
7. (c)

Answers to Part 2. Completion

8. Multipolar
9. Cell body
10. Myelin sheath
11. Neuroglia
12. Neurolemma
13. Axon collateral
14. Dendrite
15. Association
16. Bipolar
17. Neurofibril node
18. Oligodendrocyte
19. Effector
20. Synapse
21. Reverberating

13
Nervous System

1. Materials Needed:

Textbook of anatomy and physiology
Torso
Charts, models, and preserved specimens of human:
  Brain and spinal cord
Charts, models, slides, and preserved specimens of human:
  Cranial nerves
  Spinal nerves
Compound microscope
Lens paper
Prepared slides of:
  The spinal cord
  Nerve trunk in transverse section
Oscilloscope
Multi-choice reaction timer (Stoelting Co., Chicago, IL)
EEG electrodes
EEG selector box
Electrode jelly
Stretchable Band-Aids®
Dishwashing pad
Flashlight
Reflex hammer
Perfume
Oil of cloves
Garlic
Snellen eye chart
Cotton-tipped applicators
10% salt solution
10% sugar solution
Tongue depressor
Bone saw
Bone cutting forceps
Dissecting instruments and trays
Rubber gloves
Laboratory coat
Biostat
Hand lens
Preserved sheep brain with cranial nerves
Double-injected preserved cats or just preserved cat brains (with cranial nerves) and spinal cords (with spinal nerves)

2. Suggested Audiovisual Materials

Videocassettes

Dream Voyage (26 min; C; Sd; 1990; FHS)
Dreams: Theater of the Night (26 min; C; Sd; 1990; FHS)
Experiments in Human Behavior (filmstrip on video; 1990; HRM)
Exploring the Brain: The Newest Frontier (filmstrip on video; 1991; HRM)
Human Facial Expression (15 min; C; Sd; 1990; FHS)
Inside Information: The Brain and How It Works (58 min; C; Sd; 1992; FHS)
Insomnia (19 min; C; Sd; 1992; FHS)
Is Your Brain Really Necessary? (50 min; C; Sd; 1992; FHS)
Moving Parts (26 min; C; Sd; 1990; FHS)
Mysteries of the Mind (26 min; C; Sd; 1990; FHS)
Our Talented Brain (26 min; C; Sd; 1990; FHS)
Simulated Intelligence (28 min; C; Sd; 1992; FHS)
Theater of the Night: The Science of Sleep and Dreams (filmstrip on video; 1991; HRM)
The Brain (29 min; C; Sd; 1990; IM)
The Brain and How It Works (58 min; C; Sd; 1992; FHS)
The Brain Machine (artificial intelligence) (26 min; C; Sd; 1992; FHS)
The Development of the Human Brain (40 min; C; Sd; 1990; FHS)
The Enchanted Loom (cerebral interpretation} (26 min; C; Sd; 1990; FHS)
The Human Brain. 2nd edition (24 min; C; Sd; 1990; GA)
The Living Cell (neurons and the brain) (26 min: C; Sd; 1992; FHS)
The Nature of Memory (26 min; C; Sd: 1990; FHS)
The Sexual Brain (26 min; C; Sd; 1990; FHS)
What Makes Us Tick? {development of personality] (24 min; C; Sd; 1990; FHS)

Films: 16 mm

Fundamentals of the Nervous System (16 min; BW; Sd; EBEC/KSU)
Spinal Nerves (I8 min; C; Sd; 1976: UTEX)
Basic Anatomy and Physiology of the Mammal: The Nervous System (7 min; C; Sd; UIFC)
How The Mind Begins (24 min; C; Sd; TGC)
Human Brain (10 min; BW; SD; TGC)
Marvels of the Brain (23 min; C; Sd; NGF)
Nervous System in Man (18 min; C; Sd; IU)
Secrets of the Brain (15 min; C; Sd; CFI)
The Mind of Man (119 min; C; Sd; UIFC)
Glands of the Head, Part VI (13 min; C; Sd; TNF)
Parasympathetic and Sympathetic Innervation. , Parts I & II (40 min; C; Sd; TNF)

Transparencies: 35 mm

Nervous System and Its Function (20 slides: EI/CONN)
Neurotransmitters (75 slides; IBIS)
Psychobiology: The Brain and Behavior (150 slides: CFH/CARO)

Transparencies: overhead projection

Human Spinal Cord (CARO)
Human Brain Anatomy. Parts l-2 (2 transparencies; CARO)
Nervous System: Brain (GAF)
Nervous System (GSC)
Nervous System — Unit 5 (RJB)
Autonomic Nervous System (GAF)
The Autonomic Nervous System (1 transparency with 3 overlays; CARO)

Computer Software

Body Language: Nervous System {anatomy} (IBM, Macintosh; PLP)
Dynamic of the Human Nervous System (IBM; EI)
Flash: Nerves (IBM; PLP)
Alcohol: Making the Choice (IBM; PLP)
Body Language: Nervous System (anatomy) (IBM, Macintosh; PLP)
Drinking and Not Drinking Alcohol (IBM PC; CARO)
Drug Abuse (IBM, Mac; EI)
Dynamics of the Human Nervous System (IBM; EI)
Flash: Nerves (IBM; PLP)
Flash: The EEG (IBM; PLP)
Keep Off the Grass: Marijuana (IBM ; CARO)

3. Answers to Illustrations and/or Questions:

Answers to Figure 13.1 (a) and (b)

1. Dura mater
2. Arachnoid
3. Pia mater
4. Subarachnoid space
5. Denticulate ligament
6. Posterior gray horn
7. Lateral gray horn
8. Anterior gray horn
9. Anterior white column
10. Gray commissure
11. Lateral white column
12. Central canal
13. Posterior white column
14. Cervical plexus

Answers to Figure 13.2

1. Cervical nerves
2. Thoracic nerves
3. Cauda equina
4. Lumbar nerves
5. Sacral nerves
6. Coccygeal nerves
7. Filum terminale
8. Sacral plexus
9. Lumbar plexus
10. Conus medullaris
11. Lumbar enlargement
12. Brachial plexus
13. Cervical enlargement
14. Cervical plexus

Answers to Figure 13.3

1. Posterior root
2. Axon of sensory neuron
3. Cell body of sensory neuron
4. Axon of motor neuron
5. Cell body of motor neuron
6. Anterior root
7. Spinal nerve
8. Posterior root ganglion

Answers to Figure 13.4

Epineurium
Perineurium
3. Fascicle
4. Endoneurium

Answers to Figure 13.5

Segmental branch
Lesser occipital
Greater auricular
Transverse cervical
5. Ansa cervicalis
6. Supraclavicular
7. Phrenic

Answers to Figure 13.6 (a)

Dorsal scapular
Nerve to subclavius
Suprascapular
Axillary
Radial
Lower subscapular
Thoracodorsal
Medial pectoral
9. Lateral pectoral
10. Musculocutaneous
11. Median
12. Ulnar
13. Medial antebrachial cutaneous
14. Medial brachial cutaneous
15. Long thoracic
16. Upper scapular

Answers to Figure 13.6 (b)

Axillary
Musculocutaneous
Radial
4. Median
5. Ulnar

Answers to Figure 13.7

Iliohypogastric
Ilioinguinal
Genitofemoral
4. Lateral femoral cutaneous
5. Femoral
6. Obturator

Answers to Figure 13.8 (a)

Superior gluteal
Inferior gluteal
Common peroneal
Tibial
Sciatic
Nerve to quadriceps femoris and inferior gemellus
7. Nerve to obturator internus and superior gemellus
8. Posterior femoral cutaneous
9. Pudendal

Answers to Figure 13.8 (b)

Pudendal
Sciatic
Tibial
Common peroneal
5. Deep peroneal
6. Superficial peroneal
7. Medial plantar
8. Lateral plantar

Answers to Table 13.7 Nerves of Plexuses and Their Innervations

Nerve	Plexus	Innervation
Musculocutaneous	Brachial	Coracobrachialis, biceps brachii, and brachialis
Femoral	Lumbar	Flexor muscles of thigh, extensor muscles of leg, skin on anterior and medial aspect of thigh and medial side of leg and foot
Phrenic	Cervical	Diaphragm
Pudendal	Sacral	Muscles of perineum, skin of penis and scrotum in male, and clitoris, labi majora, labia minora, and lower vagina in female
Axillary	Brachial	Deltoid and teres minor muscles; skin over deltoid and superior, posterio aspect of arm
Transverse cervical	Cervical	Skin over anterior aspect of neck
Radial	Brachial	Extensor muscles of arm and forearm, skin of posterior arm and forearm, lateral two-thirds of dorsum of hand, and fingers over proximal and middle phalanges
Obturator	Lumbar	Adductor muscles of leg and skin over medial aspect of thigh
Tibial	Sacral	Gastrocnemius, plantaris, soleus, popliteus, tibialis posterior, flexor digitorum, and flexor hallicus longus
Thoracodorsal	Brachial	Latissimus dorsi muscle
Perforating cutaneous	Sacral	Skin over inferior medial aspect of buttock
Ulnar	Brachial	Flexor carpi ulnaris, flexor digitorum profundus muscles, and skin of medial side of hand, little finger, and medial half of ring finger
Long thoracic	Brachial	Serratus anterior muscle
Median	Brachial	Flexors of forearm and skin of lateral two-thirds of palm and fingers
Iliogastric	Lumbar	Muscles of anterolateral abdominal wall and skin of lower abdomen and buttock
Deep peroneal	Sacral	Tibialis anterior, extensor hallucis longus, peroneus tertius, and extensor digitorum longus and brevis muscles and skin over great and second toe
Ansa cervicalis	Cervical	Infrahyoid and geniohyoid muscles
Sciatic	Sacral	Muscles and skin of lower limbs

Answers to Figure 13.9

1. Fasciculus gracilis
2. Fasciculus cuneatus
3. Posterior spinocerebellar
4. Anterior spinocerebellar
5. Lateral spinothalamic
6. Anterior spinothalamic
7. Anterior corticospinal
8. Tectospinal
9. Vestibulospinal
10. Lateral reticulospinal
11. Rubrospinal
12. Lateral corticospinal
13. Medial reticulospinal

Answers to Table 13.2 (a) Sensory (Ascending) Tracts

Tract	*Functions*
Posterior Column (Fasciculus Gracilis and Fasciculus Cuneatus)	Conveys nerve impulses for conscious proprioception and tactile sensations from one side of the body to the medulla oblongata on the same side. The first-order neurons that form the posterior column convey the sensations of light touch, two-point discrimination, stereognosis (ability) to recognize an object by feeling it); conscious proprioception (awareness of position of limbs and other body parts); kinesthesia (awareness of direction of movement of limbs and other body parts); weight discrimination (ability to assess weight of an object); and vibration. From the medulla. the axons of second-order neurons decussate (cross over) to the contralateral (opposite) side and form the medial lemniscus, which carries nerve impulses to the thalamus in the opposite cerebral hemisphere. Third-order neurons transmit nerve impulses from the thalamus to the somatosensory cortex, also in the contralateral cerebral hemisphere.
Lateral spinothalamic	Conveys nerve impulses for pain and thermalsomatic sensations from one side of the body to the thalamus on the opposite side. The second-order axons that form this tract receive input from first-order neurons on the opposite side. From the thalamus, third-order neurons carry nerve impulses to the somatosensory cortex, also in the contralateral cerebral hemisphere.
Anterior spinothalamic	Conveys nerve impulses for somatic sensations of tickle; itch; crude, poorly localized touch; and pressure from one side of the body to the thalamus on the opposite side. The second-order axons that form this tract receive input from first-order neurons on the opposite side. From the thalmus, third order neurons carry nerve impulses to the somatosensory area of the cortex, also in the contralateral cerebral hemisphere.

Answers to Table 13.2 (a) Sensory (Ascending) Tracts (continued)

Tract	*Functions*
Posterior spinocerebellar	Conveys nerve impulses for subconscious proprioception from the trunk and lower limb of one side of the body to same side of cerebellum. The second-order axons that form this tract receive input from first-order neurons on the same side, ascend to the medulla, and pass through the inferior cerebellar peduncle into the cerebellum on the same side. This sensory input keeps the cerebellum informed of actual movements and allows it to coordinate, smooth, and refine skilled movements and maintain posture and balance.
Anterior spinocerebellar	Conveys nerve impulses for subconscious proprioception from the trunk and lower limb of one side of the body to the ipsilateral cerebellum. The second-order axons that form this tract receive input from first-order neurons on the opposite side, ascend to the medulla, and pass through the superior cerebellar peduncle into the cerebellum on the same side. Before terminating, however, the axons recross with the cerebellum, thus coveying proprioceptive information from one side of the body to the cerebellum on the same side.

Answers to Table 13.2 (b) Motor (Descending) Tracts

Tract	*Functions*
Pyramidal	
Lateral corticospinal	Conveys nerve impulses from the motor cortex to skeletal muscles on opposite side of body to coordinate precise, discrete, voluntary movements, especially of the hands and feet. Axons of upper motor neurons (UMNs) descend from the cortex into the medulla. Here, 90% cross over to the opposite side (decussate)and then enter the contralateral spinal cord to form this tract. At their level of termination, these UMNs enter the anterior horn of the spinal cord on the same side and provide input to lower motor neurons (LMNs), which provide motor output to skeletal muscles. 55% of the UMNs terminate in the cervical cord (supplying muscles of the upper limbs), 20% in the thoracic cord, and 25% in the lumbrosacral cord (supplying muscles of the lower limbs). This tract comprises approximately 92% of the descending, pyramidal motor fibers.
Anterior corticospinal	Conveys nerve impulses from the motor cortex to skeletal muscles on opposite side of body to coordinate movements of the axial skeleton. Axons of upper motor neurons (UMNs) descend from the cortex into the medulla. Here, the 10% that do not cross over enter the spinal cord and form this tract. At their level of termination, these UMNs enter the spinal cord anterior gray horn on the opposite side and provide input to lower motor neurons, which provide motor output to skeletal muscles. This tract carries approximately 8% of the descending, pyramidal motor fibers.
Corticobulbar	Conveys nerve impulses from the motor cortex to skeletal muscles of the head and neck to coordinate precise, discrete, voluntary contractions. Axons of upper motor neurons descend from the cortex into the brain stem, where some cross to the opposite side, while others remain uncrossed. They provide input to lower motor neurons in the nuclei of cranial nerves III, IV, V, VI, VII, IX, X, XI, and XII, which control voluntary movements of the eyes, tongue and neck; chewing; facial expression; and speech.

Answers to Table 13.2 (b) Motor (Descending) Tracts (continued)

Tract	*Functions*
Extrapyramidal	
Rubrospinal	Conveys motor impulses from the red nucleus, which receives input from the cortex and cerebellum, to skeletal muscles on the opposite side of the body. UMNs decussate immediately within the mesencephalon and travel to all levels of the spinal cord to synapse with LMNs. This tract is thought to be involved in control of flexor and extensor muscle control, particularly involving movements of the distal limbs.
Tectospinal	Conveys motor impulses from the superior colliculus to skeletal muscles on the contralateral side of the body that move the head and eyes in response to visual stimuli.
Vestibulospinal	Conveys motor impulses from the vestibular nuclei, which receives input about head movements from the vestibular apparatus in the inner ear. This tract remains ipsilateral for its entire length, and is thought to regulate muscle tone for maintaining balance.
Lateral reticulospinal	Conveys motor impulses from the reticular formation to muscles that facilitate flexor reflexes, inhibit extensor reflexes, and decrease muscle tone in muscles of the axial skeleton and proximal limbs. Most of the fibers of this tract remain ipsilateral, but some fibers do decussate to the opposite side.
Medial reticulospinal	Conveys motor impulses from the pons that facilitate extensor reflexes. inhibit flexor reflexes. and increase muscle tone in muscles of the axial skeleton and proximal limbs. Most of the fibers of this tract remain ipsilateral, but some fibers do decussate to the opposite side.

Answers to Figure 13.10 (a) and (b)

. Cerebrum
. Thalamus
. Hypothalamus
. Diencephalon
. Midbrain

6. Pons
7. Medulla oblongata
8. Brain stem
9. Cerebellum

Answers to Figure 13.11

. Arachnoid villus
. Superior sagittal sinus
. Choroid plexus of lateral ventricle
. Lateral ventricle
. Interventricular foramen
. Pia mater
. Arachnoid
. Dura mater

9. Third ventricle
10. Choroid plexus of third ventricle
11. Lateral aperture
12. Subarachnoid space of spinal cord
13. Median aperture
14. Fourth ventricle
15. Choroid plexus of fourth ventricle
16. Cerebral aqueduct

Answers to Figure 13.12

. Interventricular foramen
. Cerebral aqueduct
. Fourth ventricle

4. Subarachnoid space
5. Arachnoid villi of dural venous sinuses

Answers to Figure 13.13

. Medial geniculate nucleus
. Lateral geniculate nucleus
. Ventral posterior nuclei

4. Ventral lateral nucleus
5. Ventral anterior nucleus

Answers to Figure 13.14 (a)

. Frontal lobe
. Insula
. Temporal lobe

4. Occipital lobe
5. Parietal lobe

Answers to Figure 13.14 (b)

. Frontal lobe
. Temporal lobe

3. Occipital lobe
4. Parietal lobe

Answers to Figure 13.15

. Primary somatosensory area
. Primary motor area
. Premotor area
. Frontal eye field area
. Motor speech (Broca's) area
. Primary gustatory area

7. Primary auditory area
8. Auditory association area
9. Primary visual area
10. Visual association area
11. Somatosensory association area

Answers to Figure 13.16

1. Projection fibers
2. Corpus callosum
3. Anterior commissure
4. Posterior commissure
5. Commissural fibers
6. Association fibers

Answers to Figure 13.17

1. Caudate nucleus
2. Putamen
3. Globus pallidus
4. Lentiform nucleus
5. Corpus striatum

Answers to Figure 13.18 (a) through (c)

1. Anterior lobe
2. Posterior lobe
3. Vermis
4. Cerebellar peduncles
5. Flocculonodular lobe
6. Folia
7. Cerebellar nucleus
8. Arbor vitae
9. Cerebellar cortex

Answers to Figure 13.19 (a)

1. Olfactory bulb
2. Optic (II) nerve
3. Oculomotor (III) nerve
4. Trochlear (IV) nerve
5. Trigeminal (V) nerve
6. Abducens (VI) nerve
7. Facial (VII) nerve
8. Vestibulocochlear (VIII) nerve
9. Glosspharyngeal (IX) nerve
10. Vagus (X) nerve
11. Accessory (XI) nerve
12. Hypoglossal (XII) nerve

Answers to Figure 13.19 (b)

1. Longitudinal fissure
2. Optic (II) nerve
3. Cerebrum
4. Pons
5. Cerebellum
6. Spinal cord
7. Medulla oblongata
8. Optic chiasm
9. Olfactory tract
10. Olfactory bulb

Answers to Figure 13.25

1. Cell body of preganglionic neuron
2. Cell body of postganglionic neuron
3. Autonomic ganglion
4. Visceral effector
5. Axon of postganglionic neuron
6. Axon of preganglionic neuron

Answers to Table 13.1 Activities of the Autonomic Nervous System

Visceral Effector	*Effect of Sympathetic Stimulation* (α or β receptors, except as noted)*	*Effect of Parasympathetic Simulation (Muscarinic receptors)*
Glands		
Sweat	Increases secretion locally on palms and soles (α); increases secretion in most body regions (muscarinic ACh receptors)	None
Lacrimal (tear)	None	Stimulates secretion
Adrenal medulla	Promotes epinephrine and norepinephrine secretion (nicotinic and ACh receptors)	None
Liver	Promotes conversion of glycogen in the liver into glucose (glycogenolysis), stimulates conversion of noncarbohydrates in the liver into glucose (gluconeogenesis), and decreases bile secretion (α and β_2)	Promotes glycogen synthesis; increases bile secretion
Kidney: juxta-glomular cells	Stimulates secretion of renin (β_1)	None
Pancreas	Inhibits secretion of digestive enzymes and insulin (α); promotes secretion of glucagon (β_2)	Promotes secretion of digestive enzymes and insulin
Smooth Muscle		
Iris, radial muscle	Contraction → dilation of pupil (α)	None
Iris, circular muscle	None	Contraction → constriction of pupil
Ciliary muscle of the eye	Relaxation for far vision (β_2)	Contraction for near vision
Salivary gland arterioles	Vasoconstriction, which decreases secretion of saliva (β_2)	Vasodilation, which increases K^+ and water secretion
Gastric gland arterioles	Vasoconstriction, which inhibits secretion (β_2)	Promotes secretion
Intestinal gland arterioles	Vasoconstriction, which inhibits secretion (α)	Promotes secretion
Lungs, bronchial muscle	Relaxation → airway dilation (β_2)	Contraction → airway constriction

Answers to Table 13.1 Activities of the Autonomic Nervous System (continued)

Visceral Effector	Effect of Sympathetic Stimulation (α or β receptors, except as noted)*	Effect of Parasympathetic Simulation (Muscarinic receptors)
Heart arterioles	Relaxation → dilation of coronary vessels (β_1)	Contraction → constriction of coronary vessels
Skin and mucosal arterioles	Contraction → constriction (α)	Dilation, which may not be physiologically significant
Skeletal muscle arterioles	Contraction → constriction (α); Relaxation → dilation (β_2) Relaxation → dilation (muscarinic)	None
Abdominal visceral arterioles	Contraction → constriction (α,β)	None
Brain arterioles	Slight contraction → constriction (α)	None
Systemic veins	Contraction → constriction (α) Relaxation → dilation (β_2)	None
Gallbladder and ducts	Relaxation (β_2)	Contraction → increased release of bile into small intestine
Stomach and intestines	Decreases motility and tone (α,β_2); contracts sphincters (α)	Increases motility and tone; relaxes sphincters → enhanced digestive activities and defecation
Kidney	Constriction of blood vessels → decreases rate of urine production (α)	None
Ureter	Increases motility	Decreases motility
Spleen	Contraction and discharge of stored blood into general circulation (α)	None
Urinary bladder	Relaxation of muscular wall (α); contraction of trigone and sphincter (α)	Contraction of muscular wall; relaxation of trigone and sphincter → urination
Uterus	Inhibits contraction in nonpregnant women (β_2); promotes contraction in pregnant women (α)	Minimal effect
Sex organs	In male: contraction of smooth muscle of ductus (vas) deferens, seminal vesicle, prostate → ejaculation	Vasodilation and erection in both sexes
Hair follicles (arrctor pili muscle)	Contraction → erection of hairs in skin	None

*Subcategories of β receptors are listed where known

4. Answers to Laboratory Report Questions:

Answers to Part 1. Multiple Choice

1. (b)
2. (c)
3. (d)
4. (a)
5. (c)
6. (a)
7. (d)
8. (a)
9. (b)
10. (d)
11. (c)
12. (c)
13. (a)
14. (d)
15. (c)
16. (d)
17. (b)
18. (d)

Answers to Part 2. Completion

19. Posterior median sulcus
20. Epidural space
21. Posterior root ganglion
22. Epineurium
23. Arachnoid
24. Medulla oblongata
25. Midbrain
26. Pons
27. Sulcus
28. Central sulcus
29. Arbor vitae
30. Subdural space
31. Diencephalon
32. Cerebral aqueduct
33. Transverse
34. Rami communicantes
35. Sacral
36. 31
37. Cerebellum
38. Postganglionic
39. Sympathetic
40. Vertebral (collateral)
41. Phrenic
42. Anterior spinothalamic
43. Femoral
44. Rubrospinal
45. Radial
46. Primary somatosensory area
47. Motor speech (Broca's) area
48. White matter
49. General visceral efferent
50. Second
51. Thalamus
52. Adrenergic

Answers to Part 3. Matching

53. S
54. L
55. B
56. C
57. B
58. L
59. S
60. S
61. L
62. B
63. C

Answers to Part 3. Matching

64. C
65. A
66. E
67. F
68. B
69. G
70. D

14
Sensory Receptors and Sensory Motor Pathways

1. Materials Needed:

Textbook of anatomy and physiology
Compound microscope
Lens paper
Hand lens
Opthalmoscope
Otoscope
Colored felt marking pen
Compass
Von Frey's hair or bristle
Colored chalk
Forceps or metal probe
Ice water
Water bath
Thermometer
One-liter breakers
Cotton
Dissecting probe
Shallow pan
Millimeter ruler
Torso
Charts. models. slides, and preserved specimens of human:
- Nose
- Tongue
- Accessory structures of the eye
- Eyeball I
- Ear

Prepared slides of:
- Tactile receptors
  - corpuscles of touch (Meissner's)
  - tactile (Merkel) discs
  - hair root plexuses
  - free (naked) nerve endings
  - lamellated (Pacinian) corpuscles
  - type II cutaneous mechanoreceptors (organs of Ruffini)]

Proprioceptive receptors
- joint kinesthetic receptors
- muscle spindles
- tendon (Golgi) organs

Olfactory epithelium
Taste buds
Spiral organ (organ of Corti)

Granulated sugar
3% sugar solution (3 g of sugar/l00 mL of water; serves 24 students)

.5% quinine or Epsom salt solution (0.5 g of quinine or Epsom salts/100 mL of water: serves 24 students)
0.5% vinegar or acetic acid solution (0.5 g of acetic acid/100 mL of water; serves 24 students)
5% salt solution (5 g of NaCl/100 mL of water: serves 24 students)
Alcohol
Phenylthiocarbamide (PTC) crystals or paper
Small cubes of carrot, onion, potato, and apple
Snellen eye chart
Index card, 3" x 5"
Ruler, yardstick, tape measure, or meter stick
Pencil, paper, and a book
Depth perception tester
Red cross or red marker
Ischihara plates or Homgren test
Audiometer
Lamp or flashlight
Mallet
Tuning fork
Card with printer letter
Ticking watch
Cotton-tipped applicators
Cotton plugs
Preserved vertebrate (beef or sheep) eye
Dissecting instruments and trays
Rubber gloves
Laboratory coat
Biostat

2. Suggested Audiovisual Materials

Videocassettes

Eyes and Ears (26 min; C; Sd; FHS)
Moving Parts (26 min; C; Sd; FHS)
Dreams: Theater of the Mind (28 min; C; Sd; FHS)
Dream Voyage (26 min; C; Sd; FHS)
Memory: Fabric of the Mind (28 min; C; Sd; FHS)

Films: 16 mm

The Secrets of Sleep (53 min; C; Sd; UIFC)
Sleep: Dream Voyage (26 min; C; Sd; FHS)
Pain (30 min; C; Sd; TLV)
Skin Deep (26 min; C; Sd; TLV)
The Keys of Paradise (57 min; C; Sd; TLV)
Nervous System in Man (18 min; C; Sd; IU)
The Senses (BW; McG)
The Nose: Structure and Function (11 min; C; Sd; EBEC)
More Than Meets the Eye (30 min; C; Sd; TLV)
The Eye: Part V (21 min; TNF)
The Eye: An Inside Story (10 min; C; Sd; UIFC)

Films: 8 mm

Sense of Hearing: The Ear: Its Structure and Function; The Ear: Perception of Sound; The Eye: Visual Accommodation: The Eye: Nearsightedness; The Eye: Farsightedness (all C; Si; H&B)
Human Skin (C; H&B)

Transparencies: 35 mm

Histology of the Sensory System (EIL)
Eyes and Their Function (20 slides; EIL)
Ears and Their Function (20 slides; EIL)
Touch, Taste, and Smell (20 slides; EIL)
Organs of Special Senses (40 slides; CARO)

Transparencies: overhead projection

Taste and Smell (CARO)
The Eye (CARO)
Human Eye (CARO)
The Ear (CARO)
Human Ear I & 2 (CARO)
The Hearing Process (CARO)
Special Senses- Unit 3 (C; 14 transparencies; RJB)
Eye; Ear (both GAF)
Structure of the Eye (TSED)
Eye (HSC)
Human Skin Histology (CARO)

3. Answers to Illustrations and/or Questions:

Answers to Figure 14.1

1. Lungs and diaphragm
2. Heart
3. Pancreas
4. Stomach
5. Ovaries
6. Colon
7. Urinary bladder
8. Ureter
9. Kidney
10. Appendix
11. Small intestine
12. Liver and gallbladder

Answers to Figure 14.2

1. Third-order neuron
2. Second-order neuron
3. First-order neuron
4. Fasciculus gracilis
5. Fasciculus cuneatus
6. Nucleus cuneatus
7. Nucleus gracilis

Answers to Figure 14.3

1. Third-order neuron
2. Second-order neuron
3. First-order neuron
4. Lateral spinothalamic tract

Answers to Figure 14.4

1. Third-order neuron
2. Second-order neuron
3. First-order neuron
4. Anterior spinothalamic tract

Answers to Figure 14.5 (a) and (b)

1. Olfactory tract
2. Olfactory bulb
3. Olfactory nerve fiber
4. Olfactory (Bowman's) gland
5. Basal cell
6. Olfactory receptor
7. Supporting (sustentacular) cell
8. Dendrite
9. Olfactory hairs

Answers to Figure 14.6

1. Supporting (sustentacular) cell
2. Olfactory receptor
3. Basal cell

Answers to Figure 14.7 (a)

1. Gustatory pore
2. Gustatory hair
3. Gustatory receptor
4. Supporting (sustentacular) cell

Answers to Figure 14.7 (b)

1. Gustatory pore
2. Gustatory receptor
3. Supporting (sustentacular) cell
4. Basal cell

Answers to Figure 14.8

1. Lacrimal punctum
2. Lacrimal sac
3. Lacrimal gland
4. Excretory lacrimal duct
5. Lacrimal canals
6. Nasolacrimal duct

Answers to Figure 14.9 (a)

1. Ciliary body and muscle
2. Suspensory ligament
3. Scleral venous sinus (canal of Schlemm)
4. Posterior chamber
5. Anterior chamber
6. Anterior cavity
7. Pupil
8. Iris
9. Lens
10. Cornea
11. Ora serrata
12. Sclera
13. Choroid
14. Retina (nervous tunic)
15. Optic (II) nerve
16. Optic disc (blind spot)
17. Central fovea
18. Macula lutea
19. Vitreous chamber (posterior cavity)

Answers to Figure 14.12

1. Optic (II) nerve
2. Optic chiasm
3. Optic tract
4. Thalamus
5. Occipital lobe of cerebral cortex

Answers to Figure 14.13

1. Optic (II) nerve
2. Malleus
3. Incus
4. Round window
5. Auditory (Eustachian) tube
4. Eardrum (tympanic membrane)
8. External auditory canal (meatus)
9. Lobule
10. Helix
11. Auricle

Answers to Figure 14.14

1. Oval window
2. Round window
3. Stapes
4. Incus
5. Malleus

Answers to Figure 14.15

1. Semicircular ducts
2. Ampullae
3. Utricle
4. Saccule
5. Cochlea
6. Vestibule

Answers to Figure 14.16

1. Scala vestibuli
2. Scala tympani
3. Basilar membrane
4. Hair cells of spiral organ (organ of Corti)
5. Tectorial membrane
6. Cochlear duct (scala media)
7. Vestibular membrane

Answers to Figure 14.17 (a) and (b)

1. Tectorial membrane
2. Inner hair cell
3. Outer hair cell
4. Basilar membrane
5. Vestibular membrane

Answers to Figure 14.19 (a)

1. Otoliths
2. Otolithic membrane
3. Supporting cell
4. Hair (receptor) cell

Answers to Figure 14.19 (b)

1. Capula
2. Supporting cell
3. Hair (receptor) cell

Answers to Figure 14.20

1. Upper motor neurons
2. Decussation in medulla
3. Anterior corticospinal tract
4. Lower motor neurons
5. Lateral corticospinal tract

4. Answers to Laboratory Report Questions:

Answers to Part 1. Multiple Choice

1. (a)
2. (d)
3. (b)
4. (b)
5. (a)
6. (c)
7. (b)
8. (b)
9. (c)
10. (c)
11. (a)
12. (d)
13. (a)
14. (c)
15. (a)
16. (d)
17. (c)
18. (b)
19. (c)
20. (a)
21. (d)
22. (b)
23. (a)
24. (b)
25. (c)
26. (a)
27. (d)
28. (c)
29. (b)
30. (d)

Answers to Part 2. Completion

31. Interoceptors (visceroceptors)
32. Lacrimal apparatus
33. Ganglion cell layer
34. Blind spot (optic disc)
35. Glaucoma
36. Optic tract
37. Round
38. Perilymph
39. Vibration
40. Lamellated (Pacinian)
41. Joint kinesthetic receptors
42. Olfactory tract
43. Tympanic antrum
44. Eardrum (tympani membrane)
45. Endolymph
46. Vestibular membrane
47. Otolithic membrane
48. Astigmatism
49. Convergence of eyes
50. Lateral spinothalamic
51. Lateral corticospinal
52. Nociceptors
53. Discriminative touch
54. Lower motor neurons
55. Corticobulbar

15
Endocrine System

1. Materials Needed:

Textbook of anatomy and physiology
Torso
Charts of endocrine glands
Models of endocrine glands
- Pituitary gland
- Thyroid gland
- Adrenal cortex
- Adrenal medulla
- Pancreas
- Testes
- Ovary
- Thymus gland

Compound microscope
Lens paper
Immersion oil
Xylol or alcohol
Prepared slides of:
- Anterior pituitary gland
- Posterior pituitary gland
- Thyroid gland
- Parathyroid glands
- Adrenal cortex
- Adrenal medulla
- Pancreas
- Testes
- Ovaries

2. Suggested Audiovisual Materials

Videocassettes

Animal Hormones I: Principles and Functions (80 slides on video-cassette/guide; EI)
Blood Sugar Regulation and Diabetes (30 min; C; Sd; 1990; GA)
Diabetes (19 min: C; Sd; I991 ; FHS)
Diabetes (The Quiet Killer) (26 min; C: Sd: 1990; FHS)
Messengers (26 min; C; Sd; 1990; FHS)
Regulatory Systems (30 min; C; Sd; PLP)
The Chemistry of Life: Hormones and the Endocrine System (filmstrip on video; HRM/EI)

Films: 16 mm

Endocrine Glands (11 min; BW; UCEMC)
Endocrine Glands: How They Affect You (15 min; BW; McG)
Principles of Endocrine Activity (16 min; IU)

Transparencies: 35 mm

Animal Hormones I: Principles and Functions (80 slides/cassette/guide; EI)
Diabetes Medical Slide Series (82 slides: CARO)
Endocrine System (Slides 157- 172; McG)
Endocrine System and Its Function (20 slides; EVCON)
Histology of the Endocrine System (EI)
Hormones (22 slides/guide; EI)
Hormones (40 slides; CARO)
Hormones and the Endocrine System, Parts 1-4 (224 slides; IBIS)
Mammalian Histology: Endocrine System (20 slides/guide; EI)
Managing Stress, Anxiety, and Frustration. Parts 1-4 (302 slides; IBIS)
Stress and Disease, Parts 1, 2 (148 slides; IBIS)
The Chemistry of Life: Hormones & the Endocrine System (224 slides/cassettes/guide; EI)
The Endocrine System Set (20 slides; CARO)
Visual Approach to Histology: Endocrine Glands (10 slides; FAD)

Transparencies: overhead projection

Activity of Trophic Hormone (K&E)
Endocrine System (GAF)
Endocrine System-Unit 10 (C, 11 transparencies; RJB)

Computer Software

Dynamics of the Human Endocrine System (IBM; EI)
Graphic Human Anatomy and Physiology Tutor: Endocrine System (IBM; PLP)
Nervous and Hormonal Systems (IBM, Macintosh; QUEUE)

3. Answers to Illustrations and/or Questions:

Answers to Figure 15.1

1. Pituitary gland (hypophysis)
2. Thyroid gland
3. Thymus gland
4. Adrenal (suprarenal) glands
5. Stomach
6. Pancreas
7. Ovaries
8. Testes
9. Small intestine
10. Kidney
11. Heart
12. Skin
13. Parathyroid glands
14. Pineal gland (epiphysis cerebri)
15. Hypothalamus

Answers to B.2. Hormones of Pituitary Gland

a. Hormones Secreted by the Anterior Pituitary Gland

Name	Major Functions
Human growth hormone (hGH); also called somatotropin and somatotropic hormone (STH)	Stimulates liver, muscle, cartilage, bone and other tissues to synthesize and secrete insulin-like growth factors (IGSs); IFGs promote growth of body cells, protein anabolism, tissue repair, lipolysis and elevation of blood glucose concentration
Thyroid-stimulating hormone (TSH); also called thyrotropin	Stimulates synthesis and secretion of hormones (T_3 and T_4) produced by thyroid gland
Adrenocorticotropic hormone (ACTH)	Stimulates production and secretion of certain adrenal cortex hormones (glucocorticoids, mainly cortisol)
Follicle-stimulating hormone (FSH)	In females, initiates development of oocytes and induces ovarian secretion of estrogens. In males, stimulates testes to produce sperm.
Leutinizing hormone (LH)	In females, together with FSH, stimulates secretion of estrogens and progesterone, ovulation, and formation of corpus luteum. In males, stimulates interstitial cells in testes to develop and produce testosterone
Prolactin (PRL); also called lactogenic hormone	With other hormones, promotes milk secretion by mammary glands
Melanocytes-stimulating hormone (MSH)	Exact role in humans is not known but stimulates dispersion of melanin in melanocytes that temporarily increases skin pigmentation in amphibians

b. Hormones Stored and Released by the Posterior Pituitary Gland

Name	Major Functions
Oxytocin (OT)	Stimulates contraction of smooth muscle cells in pregnant uterus during childbirth; stimulates contraction of smooth muscle cells around glandular cells of mammary glands, causing milk ejection.
Antidiuretic hormone (ADH)	Principal effect is to conserve body water by decreasing urine volume; also decreases water loss through perspiration and raises blood pressure by constricting arterioles

Answers to Figure 15.2

1. Epithelium of follicle
2. Thyroid follicle
3. Thyroglobulin (TGB)

Answers to C.2. Hormones of the Thyroid Gland

Name	Major Functions
Thyroxine (T_4) and triiodothyronine (T_3)	Increase basal metabolic rate, stimulate synthesis of proteins, increase use of glucose for ATP production, increase lipolysis, enhance cholesterol excretion in bile, accelerate body growth, and contribute to normal development of the nervous system
Calcitonin (CT)	Decreases blood calcium and phosphate levels by inhibiting bone resorption by osteoclasts and accelerating uptake of calcium and phosphate into bone matrix

Answers to Figure 15.3

1. Oxyphil cells
2. Principal (chief) cells

Answers to D.2. Hormone of the Parathyroid Glands

Name	Major Functions
Parathyroid hormone (PTH); also called parathormone	Increases blood calcium and magnesium levels and decreases blood phosphate level by increasing rate of dietary calcium and magnesium absorption; increases number and activity of osteoclasts; increases calcium reabsorption by kidneys; increases phosphate excretion by kidneys; and promotes formation of calcitriol (active form of vitamin D)

Answers to Figure 15.4

1. Capsule
2. Zona glomerulosa
3. Zona fasciculata
4. Zona reticularis
5. Adrenal medulla

Answers to E.2. Hormones of the Adrenal Cortex

Name	Major Functions
a. Mineralocorticoids (mainly aldosterone)	Increase blood levels of sodium and water and decrease blood levels of potassium
b. Glucocorticoids (mainly cortisol)	Increase rate of protein catabolism (except in liver), stimulate gluconeogenesis and lipolysis, provide resistance to stress, dampen inflammation, and depress immune responses
c. Androgens	Levels secreted by adult males are so low in comparison to amounts produced by testes that their effects are usually insignificant. In females, adrenal androgens may contribute to sex drive and libido. They assist in early development of axillary and pubic hair in both sexes

Answers to E.4. Hormones of the Adrenal Medulla

Name	Major Functions
Epinephrine, norepinephrine (NE)	Sympathomimetic, that is , produces effects that mimic those of the sympathetic division of the autonomic nervous system (ANS) during stress

Answers to Figure 15.5

1. Beta cell
2. Alpha cell
3. Acini

Answers to F.2. Hormones of the Pancreas

Name	Major Functions
Glucagon	Raises blood glucose level by accelerating breakdown of glycogen into glucose in liver (glycogenolysis) and conversion of other nutrients into glucose in liver (gluconeogenesis) and releasing glucose into blood
Insulin	Lowers blood glucose level by accelerating transport of glucose into cells, converting glucose into glycogen (glycogenesis), and decreasing glycogenolysis and gluconeogenesis; also increases lipogenesis and stimulates protein synthesis
Somatostatin	Inhibits secretion of glucagon and insulin and slows absorption of nutrients from gastrointestinal tract
Pancreatic polypeptide	Inhibits secretion of somatostatin, contraction of the gall bladder, and secretion of pancreatic digestive enzymes

Answers to Figure 15.6

1. Basement membrane
2. Spermatogonium
3. Spermatid
4. Sperm cell
5. Lumen of seminiferous tubule
6. Interstitial endocrinocyte (Leydig cell)

Answers to G.2. Hormones of the Testes

Name	Major Functions
Testosterone	Stimulates descent of testes before birth, regulates spermatogenesis, and promotes development and maintenance of masculine secondary sex characteristics
Inhibin	Inhibits secretion of FSH from anterior pituitary gland

Answers to Figure 15.7

1. Primordial follicle
2. Primary (preantral) follicle
3. Secondary (antral) follicle
4. Tunica albuginea
5. Germinal epithelium
6. Ovarian medulla
7. Mature (Graafian) follicle
8. Ovarian cortex
9. Corpus luteum (mature)
10. Corpus albicans

Answers to G.2. Hormones of the Ovaries

Name	Major Functions
Estrogens and progesterone	Together with gonadotropic hormones of the anterior pituitary gland, they regulate the female reproductive cycle, maintain pregnancy, prepare the mammary glands for lactation, regulate oogenesis, and promote development and maintenance of feminine secondary sex characteristics.
Relaxin	Increases flexibility of pubic symphysis during pregnancy and helps dilate uterine cervix during labor and delivery
Inhibin	Inhibits secretion of FSH from anterior pituitary gland

Answers to I.2. Hormone of the Pineal Gland

Name	Major Functions
Melatonin	It is believed to assume a primary role as the regulator of the body's internal clock, as a defense against damaging free radicals, as a promoter of sleep, and as a coordinator of the hormones involved in fertility.

Answers to J.2. Hormone of the Thymus Gland

Name	Major Functions
Thymosin, thymic humeral factor (THF), thymic factor, and thymopoietin	Promotes the proliferation and maturation of T cells and may retard the aging process

Answers to K. Other Endocrine Tissues

Name	Major Functions
Gastrin	Promotes secretion of gastric juice and increases gastrointestinal motility
Secretin	Stimulates secretion of pancreatic juice and bile
Cholecystokinin (CCK)	Stimulates secretion of pancreatic juice, causes ejection of bile from the gallbladder, and induces satiety (feeling full to satisfaction)
Gastric inhibitory peptide (GIP)	Stimulates release of insulin by pancreatic beta cells, inhibits secretion of gastric juice, and decreases gastrointestinal motility

Human chorionic gonadotropin (hCG)	Stimulates continued production of progesterone by corpus luteum to maintain pregnancy
Human chorionic somatomammotropin (hCS)	Stimulates development of the mammary glands for lactation
Erythropoietin (EPO)	Stimulates red blood cell production
Calcitriol	Active form of vitamin D, which is necessary for absorption of calcium and phosphorus from gastrointestinal tract
Atria natriuretic peptide (ANP)	Decreases blood pressure

5. Answers to Laboratory Report Questions:

Answers to Part 1. Multiple Choice

1. (b)
2. (c)
3. (c)
4. (d)
5. (d)
6. (a)
7. (d)
8. (c)
9. (c)
10. (a)

Answers to Part 2. Completion

11. Infundibulum
12. Tropin
13. Corticotroph
14. Oxytocin
15. Follicles
16. Thyroxine
17. Parathyroid
18. Mineralocorticoids
19. Glucocorticoids
20. Glucagon
21. Spermatogonia
22. Interstitial endocrinocytes Leydig cells)
23. Ovarian
24. Estrogens
25. Thymus
26. Gonadotropic
27. ADH
28. Zona reticularis
29. Chromaffin
30. Pancreatic islets (islets of Langerhanss)
31. Hypothalamus
32. Gonadotroph
33. Corpus luteum
34. Brain sand
35. Heterocrine

16
Blood

1. Materials Needed:

Textbook of anatomy and physiology
Lens paper
Immersion oil
Xylol or alcohol
Prepared slides of blood (e.g. Wright stain)
Colored charts of stained blood
Laboratory coat

B. Plasma Tests

Blood plasma or whole blood from a clinical laboratory that has been tested and certified as noninfectious or from a mammal (other than a human). Certified whole blood may be obtained from Carolina Biological Supply Company (I-800-334-555 1).
Centrifuge
Pasteur pipette attached to a bulb
Pyrex® test tubes
Test tube holders
pH paper
Hot plate and beaker
Prepared slides and colored charts of stained blood smear (e.g., Wright stain)
Laboratory coat
Forceps
Filter paper, funnel, and graduated cylinders
Rubber gloves and safety goggles
Fresh 10% bleach solution
Appropriate biohazard container
Distilled water
0.1 N HCl
10% acetic acid
Benedict's solution
Biuret reagent
Clinitest tablets

D. Red Blood Cell Tests

2. Filling of Hematocytometer (counting chamber)

Blood from a clinical laboratory that has been tested and certified as noninfectious or from a mammal (other than a human)
Hemocytometer (Neubauer is recommended) and cover slip
Unopette® Reservoir System
Rubber gloves and safety goggles
Fresh 10% bleach solution
Appropriate biohazard container

3. Red Blood Cell Count

Ward's Simulated Blood Activity Kit (l-800-962-2660)
Blood from a clinical laboratory that has been tested and certified as
noninfectious or from a mammal (other than a human). Certified whole blood may be
obtained from Carolina Biological Supply Company (I-800-334-555 1).
Hemocytometer (Neubauer is recommended) and cover slip
Mechanical hand counter
Unopette® Reservoir System for red blood cell determination
Kimwipes or other similar tissue
Disposal container
Soap
Compound microscope equipped with 430X or 450X magnification
Rubber gloves and safety goggles
Fresh 10% bleach solution
Rubber gloves
Appropriate biohazard container

4. Red Blood Cell Volume (Hematocrit)

Blood from a clinical laboratory that had been tested and certified as
noninfectious or from a mammal (other than a human). Certified whole
blood and aseptic red blood cells may be obtained from Carolina Biological
Supply Company (I-800-334-5551).
Pre-cal microhematocrit tubes, heparinized
Readacric centrifuge
Clay-Adams Seal-ease®
Microhematocrit tube reader
Disposable capillary tube
Fresh 10% bleach solution
Rubber gloves and safety goggles
Appropriate biohazard container

5. Sedimentation Rate

Blood from a clinical laboratory that had been tested and certified as noninfectious or
from a mammal (other than a human), Certified whole blood and aseptic red blood
cells may be obtained from Carolina Biological Supply Company (1-800-334-5551).
Landau sed-rate pipette
Disposable sedimentation pipette
Landau rack
Mechanical suction device
5% sodium citrate
Acetone
Fresh 10% bleach solution
Rubber gloves and safety goggles
Appropriate biohazard container

6. Hemoglobin Determination

Blood from a clinical laboratory that has been tested and certified as
noninfectious or from a mammal (other than a human). Certified whole

blood and aseptic red blood cells may be obtained from Carolina Biological Supply Company (1-800-334-555 1).
Rubber gloves and safety goggles
Fresh 10% leach solution
Appropriate biohazard container
Lens paper or wiping tissue
Hemolysis applicators
Hemoglobinometer
Tallquist® paper and scale

8. Spectrum of Oxyhemoglobin and Reduced Hemoglobin

1 O-mL graduated cylinders
Blood from a clinical laboratory that has been tested and certified as noninfectious or from a mammal (other than a human). Certified whole blood and aseptic blood cells may be obtained from Carolina Biological Supply Company (I-800-334-5551).
Fresh 10% bleach solution
Rubber gloves and safety goggles
Appropriate biohazard container
Pyrex' test tubes
Sodium dithionite (hydrosulfite), I .O G per 100 mL
1 -mL pipettes
Kimwipes or other similar tissue
Disposal container
Soap
Compound microscope equipment with 10X and 45X (or 43X) magnification
Unopipette® st #5855. WBC/Platelet Determination for Manual Methods (if available)

F. White Blood Cell Tests

1. White Blood Cell Count

Ward's Simulated Blood Kit (I-800-962-2660)
Blood from a clinical laboratory that has been tested and certified as noninfectious or from a mammal (other than a human). Certified whole blood may be obtained from Carolina Biological Supply Company (1-800-334-5551).
Rubber gloves and safety goggles
Fresh 10% bleach solution
Hemocytometer (Neubauer is recommended) and cover slip
Mechanical hand counter
Unopette® Reservoir System for white blood cell determination
Appropriate biohazard container
Landau sed-rate pipette
Landau rack
Mechanical suction device
5% sodium citrate
Acetone

2. Differential White Blood Cell Count

Blood from a clinical laboratory that has been tested and certified as noninfectious or from a mammal (other than a human). Certified whole blood may be obtained from Carolina Biological Supply Company (1 -800-334-5551).
Fresh 10% bleach solution
Rubber gloves and safety goggles
Appropriate biohazard container
Glass slides
Staining rack
Wright's solution
Buffer solution for Wright's stain
Mechanical hand counter
Compound microscope equipped with 1000X immersion objective
Oil for oil-immersion objective
Prepared slide (Wright's stain)

G. Platelets

Ward's Simulated Blood Kit (1-800-962-2660)

I. Blood Grouping

Blood from a clinical laboratory that has been tested and certified as noninfectious or from a mammal (other than a human). Certified whole blood may be obtained from Carolina Biological Supply Company (1-800-334-5551). Also available is Ward's Simulated ABO and Rh Blood Typing Activity (1-800-962-2660).
Rubber gloves and safety goggles
Fresh 10% bleach solution
Appropriate biohazard container
Glass slides
Wax pencil
Applicators or toothpicks
Anti-A, Anti-B, and Anti-D typing sera
Slide warming box

2. Suggested Audiovisual Materials

Videocassettes

Blood (33 min; C: Sd; 1990; PLP)
Blood: River of 'Life, Mirror of Health (filmstrip on video; 1990; HRM/El)
Blood: The Microscopic Miracle. 2nd edition (22 min: C; Sd; 1990; GA)
HB Masters Sickle-Cell Anemia (23 min; C; Sd; 1992; FHS)
Life Under Pressure (26 min; C; Sd; 1990; FHS)
Living With Cancer(leukemia} (26 min; C: Sd: 1990; FHS)
The Human Body: What Can Go Wrong? — Circulatory System (43 min; C: Sd: EI/PLP)
The Life of the Red Blood Cell (10 min: C: Sd; 1990; KSU)

Films: 16 mm

Blood (14 min; IP)
Blood Grouping (21 min; ICIA)
Blueprints in the Bloodstream (57 min; TLF)
Hemoglobin (25 min; UIFC)
Secret of the White Cell (24 min; NET)
The Structure and Function of Hemoglobin (25 min; UMedia)
The Work of the Blood (14 min; EBEC/KSU)

Films: 8 mm

Blood Typing; Blood Smear Preparation (both C; Si; H&R)
Circulatory System (C; COR)

Transparencies: 35 mm

Blood Under the Microscope Medical Slide Series (214 slides; CARO)
Blood: Its Composition and Function (10 slides/cassette/guide: El)
Mammalian Histology: Blood and Lymph System (20 slides/guide: El)
Medical Photomicrographs: Hematology (100 slides/guide; El)
Sickle-Cell Anemia (CARO)
The Circulatory System Set (20 slides: CARO)
Visual Approach to Histology: Blood and Bone Marrow (I9 slides; FAD)

Transparencies: overhead projection

Circulatory System: Coagulation of' the Blood (GAF)
Constituents and Function of the Blood (CARO)
Defensive Action of the White Blood Corpuscles (CARO)
Human Blood Cell Formation (CARO)

Computer Software

Circulation (EI)
Circulation and' Respiration (IBM, Macintosh; QUEUE)
Dynamics of the Human Circulatory System (IBM; EI)

3. Answers to Illustrations and/or Questions:

(None)

4. Answers to Laboratory Report Questions:

Answers to Part 1. Multiple Choice

1. (c)
2. (d)
3. (b)
4. (a)
5. (a)
6. (a)
7. (d)
8. (d)
9. (c)
10. (b)

Answers to Part 2. Completion

11. Erythrocytes
12. Hemoglobin
13. 120 days
14. Hematocrit (Hct)
15. 0 to 6 mm per hour
16. 700:1
17. Red bone marrow
18. 250,000 to 400,000
19. Blood clotting
20. Isoantigens
21. Hemolytic disease of newborn (erythroblastosis fetalis)
22. The plasma membrane of red blood cells
23. Hemopoietic (pluripotential) stem cells

Answers to Part 3. Matching

24. D
25. B
26. A
27. E
28. H
29. C
30. I
31. G
39. G

17
Heart

1. Materials Needed:

Textbook of anatomy and physiology
Charts. models, slides. and preserved specimens of a human heart
Preserved sheep heart
Double-injected preserved cats
Dissecting instruments and trays
Rubber gloves
Laboratory coat
Biostat

2. Suggested Audiovisual Materials

Videocassettes

CPR: To Save a Life, Revision (13 min; C; Sd; 1990; GA)
Heart Disease (19 min; C; Sd: 1990; FHS)
Partners for Life: The Human Heart & Lungs (2 filmstrips on video/cassettes/guide; EI)
Physical Fitness and Exercise: Designing Your Own Plan (30 min; C; Sd; PLP)
Physical Fitness ad Exercise: Relationship to Health (30 min; C; Sd; PLP)
Physical Exercise and Health: What Does This Mean to You? (30 min; C; Sd; PLP)
The Human Body: What Can Go Wrong? (six filmstrips on video/cassettes/guide; EI)
Two Hearts That Beat as One (26 min; C; Sd; 1990; FHS)
Work of the Heart, 2nd edition (21 min; C; Sd; 1990; GA)

Films

Action of Hear Valves (19 min; SU)
Angiographic Diagnosis of Coronary Artery Disease (27 min; 1968; ACR)
Disorders of the Heart Beat (20 min; WFL)
Heart and Circulation (11 min: EBEC)
Human Body: Circulatory System (13 min; COR)
Two Original Open-Heart Surgeries (60 min; UPFL)
Why Risk a Heart Attack? (14 min; TLV)

Films: 8 mm

Biology: Heart in Action (EBEC)

Transparencies: 35 mm

Circulatory System and Its Function (20 slides: EI/CONN)
For the Sake of Your Heart, Parts 1-3 (188 slides: IBIS)
Have a Heart (CARO)
Partners for Life, Parts 1,2) (160 slides; IBIS)
Systems of the Human Body: The Circulatory System (20 slides: CARO)

Visual Approach to Histology: Cardiovascular System (2 I slides: FAD)

Transparencies: overhead projection

Human Blood Vascular System. Parts 2. 3 (CARO)
Heart anti Pulse Rate (CARO)

Computer Software

Body Language: Cardiovascular System (IBM, Macintosh; PLP)
Cardiac Muscle Mechanics (IBM; QUEUE)
Cardiovascular Fitness Lab (IBM; QUEUE)
Cardiovascular System (IBM; PLP)
Circulation (El)
Circulation and Respiration (IBM, Macintosh; QUEUE)
CPR - Cardiopulmonary Resuscitation (IBM; PLP)
Dynamics of' the Human Circulatory System (IBM; EI)
Experiments in Human Physiology [heart rate] (SSS)
Graphic Human Anatomy & Physiology Tutor: Circulatory System (IBM; PLP)
Heartlab (CDL)
Understanding Human Physiology: Cardiovascular Function (IBM; PLP)
Understanding Human Physiology: Exercise Physiology (IBM; PLP)
Your Heart (IBM; EI)

3. Answers to Illustrations and/or Questions:

Answers to Figure 17.1 (a)

1. Left border
2. Apex of heart
3. Inferior surface
4. Right border
5. Base of heart

Answers to Figure 17.1 (b)

1. Superior left point
2. Superior right point
3. Inferior right point
4. Inferior left point

Answers to Figure 17.2

1. Fibrous pericardium
2. Parietal layer of serous pericardium
3. Pericardial cavity
4. Visceral layer of serous pericardium (epicardium)
5. Myocardium
6. Endocardium

Answers to Figure 17.3 (a)

1. Arch of aorta
2. Ascending aorta
3. Left pulmonary artery
4. Pulmonary trunk
5. Left pulmonary veins
6. Left atrium
7. Left coronary artery
8. Anterior interventricular sulcus
9. Left ventricle
10. Descending aorta
11. Inferior vena cava
12. Right ventricle
13. Coronary sulcus
14. Right coronary artery
15. Right atrium
16. Right pulmonary veins
17. Right pulmonary artery
18. Superior vena cava

Answers to Figure 17.3 (b)

1. Superior vena cava
2. Ascending aorta
3. Right pulmonary artery
4. Right pulmonary veins
5. Right atrium
6. Right coronary artery
7. Right ventricle
8. Inferior vena cava
9. Posterior interventricular sulcus
10. Left ventricle
11. Coronary sinus
12. Left atrium
13. Left pulmonary veins
14. Pulmonary trunk
15. Left pulmonary artery
16. Descending aorta
17. Arch of aorta

Answers to Figure 17.3 (c)

1. Arch of aorta
2. Pulmonary trunk
3. Left auricle
4. Anterior interventricular sulcus
5. Left ventricle
6. Right ventricle
7. Right atrium
8. Superior vena cava

Answers to Figure 17.4 (a)

1. Arch of aorta
2. Left pulmonary artery
3. Left pulmonary veins
4. Left atrium
5. Aortic semilunar valve
6. Bicuspid valve
7. Left ventricle
8. Interventricular septum
9. Right ventricle
10. Papillary muscle
11. Chordae tendineae
12. Inferior vena cava (IVC)
13. Tricuspid valve
14. Right atrium
15. Fossa ovalis
16. Pulmonary semilunar valve
17. Pulmonary trunk
18. Superior vena cava (SVC)
19. Right pulmonary vein
20. Ascending aorta
21. Right pulmonary artery

Answers to Figure 17.4 (b)

1. Bicuspid (mitral) valve
2. Chordae tendineae
3. Papillary muscle
4. Left ventricle
5. Interventricular septum
6. Right ventricle

Answers to Figure 17.5 (a)

1. Left coronary
2. Circumflex branch
3. Anterior interventricular branch
4. Posterior interventricular branch
5. Marginal branch
6. Right coronary

Answers to Figure 17.5 (b)

1. Coronary sinus
2. Great cardiac
3. Middle cardiac

4. Answers to Laboratory Report Questions:

Answers to Part 1. Multiple Choice

1. (c)
2. (c)
3. (b)
4. (c)
5. (d)
6. (b)
7. (d)

Answers to Part 2. Completion

8. Tricuspid
9. Pulmonary trunk (arteries)
10. Pericardium
11. Interventricular septum
12. Auricle
13. Superior vena cava (SVC)
14. Chordae tendineae
15. Sulcus
16. Circumflex
17. Left
18. Superior left point
19. Coronary
20. Trabeculae carneae
21. Great cardiac

18
Blood Vessels

1. Materials Needed:

Textbook of anatomy and physiology
Charts, models, and slides of human blood vessels
Compound microscope
Double-injected preserved cat
Lens paper
Dissecting instruments and tray
Prepared slides of:
  Artery and vein in transverse section
Rubber gloves
Laboratory coat
Biostat

2. Suggested Audiovisual Materials

Videocassettes

Life Under Pressure (26 min; 1990; FHS/CARO)
The Human Body: What Can Go Wrong? (6 filmstrips on video with guide; El)

Films: 16 mm

Arteries and Veins (14 min; KCI)
Basic Anatomy and Physiology of the Mammal: The Circulatory System (6 min; UIFC)
Blood Circulation (15 min; EBEC)
Circulation (16 min; UWF)
Disorders of the Cardiovascular System (13 min; TR)
Heart and Circulation (11 min; EBEC)
Hypertension (20 min; AMA)

Films: 8 mm

Heart in Action: Circulation: The Flow of Blood (both C; Sd; EBEC)
Circulation of the Blood. Part I; *The Heart,* Part II: *The Arteries and Veins* (C; Si; H&R)

Transparencies: 35 mm

Circulating Blood. Blood Vessels and Bone Marrow Set (29 slides; CARO)
Circulatory System (Slides 83-1 06: McG)
Circulatory System and Its Function (20 slides: EI/CONN/CARO)
Mammalian Histology: Respiratory; Circulator; Urinary Systems (20 slides/guide; El)
Visual Approach to Histology: Circulatory System (21 slides; FAD)

Transparencies: overhead projection

Blood Circulation, Arteries. and Veins (CARO)
Cardiovascular System — Unit 6 (16 transparencies; RJB)
Circulatory System; Circulatory System: Great Vessels and the Heart; Circulatory System: Heart Pumping Cycle (all GAF)
Fetal Circulation (CARO)
Heart; Circulatory System (both HSC)
Human Blood Vascular System 1 (CARO)
Human Circulatory System: The Human Heart (both TSED)
Mammalian Circulatory System (K&E)

Computer Software

Body Language: Cardiovascular System (IBM, Macintosh; PLP)
Cardiovascular System (IBM; PLP)
Circulation (EI)
Circulation and Respiration (IBM, Macintosh; QUEUE)
Dynamics of the Human Circulatory System (IBM; EI)
Flash: Blood Vessels (IBM; PLP)
Graphic Human Anatomy and Physiology Tutor: Circulatory System (IBM; PLP)
Understanding Human Physiology: Cardiovascular Function (IBM; PLP)

3. Answers to Illustrations and/or Questions:

Answers to Figure 18.3

1. Left common carotid
2. Left subclavian
3. Arch of aorta
4. Bronchial
5. Left coronary
6. Left superior phrenic
7. Left gastric
8. Left inferior phrenic
9. Left suprarenal
10. Splenic
11. Superior mesenteric
12. Left gonadal (testicular or ovarian)
13. Inferior mesenteric
14. Left common iliac
15. Left external iliac
16. Left internal iliac
17. Abdominal aorta
18. Right renal
19. Common hepatic
20. Celiac trunk
21. Thoracic aorta
22. Posterior intercostal
23. Right coronary
24. Ascending aorta
25. Brachiocephalic trunk
26. Right subclavian
27. Right common carotid

Answers to Figure 18.4 (a)

1. Right subclavian
2. Right axillary
3. Right brachial
4. Right radial
5. Brachiocephalic
6. Right ulnar
7. Right deep palmar arch
8. Right superficial palmar arch
9. Right palmar metacarpal
10. Right common palmar digital
11. Right palmar digital

Answers to Figure 18.4 (b)

1. Basilar
2. Right internal carotid
3. Right external carotid
4. Right common carotid
5. Right vertebral

Answers to Figure 18.4 (c)

1. Anterior communicating
2. Anterior cerebral
3. Posterior communicating
4. Posterior cerebral

Answers to Table 18.3

1. Brachiocephalic trunk
2. Left common carotid
3. Left subclavian
4. Right subclavian
5. Right common carotid
6. Right axillary
7. Right brachial
8. Right ulnar
9. Right radial
10. Right superficial palmar arch
11. Right palmar digital
12. Right common palmar digital
13. Basilar

Answers to Table 18.4

1. Pericardial
2. Esophageal
3. Posterior intercostal
4. Superior phrenic

Answers to Figure 18.5 (a)

1. Left gastric
2. Left suprarenal
3. Splenic
4. Superior mesenteric
5. Left renal
6. Left gonadal (testicular or ovarian)
7. Inferior mesenteric
8. Median sacral
9. Right lumbars
10. Common hepatic
11. Celiac

Answers to Figure 18.5 (b)

1. Left gastroepiploic
2. Short gastrics
3. Left gastric
4. Splenic
5. Pancreatic
6. Gastroduodenal
7. Hepatic artery proper
8. Common hepatic
9. Right gastric
10. Esophageal branch of left gastric

Answers to Figure 18.5 (c)

1. Superior mesenteric
2. Jejunals
3. Ileals
4. Ileocolic
5. Right colic
6. Inferior pancreaticoduodenal
7. Middle colic

Answers to Figure 18.5 (d)

1. Inferior mesenteric
2. Left colic
3. Sigmoid
4. Superior rectal

Answers to Table 18.5

1. Left gastric
2. Common hepatic
3. Lumbar
4. Hepatic artery proper
5. Gastroduodenal
6. Pancreatic
7. Short gastric
8. Jejunal and ileal
9. Right colic
10. Left colic
11. Sigmoid
12. Superior rectal

Answers to Figure 18.6 (a) and (b)

1. Left common iliac
2. Right external iliac
3. Right internal iliac
4. Right femoral
5. Right popliteal
6. Right anterior tibial
7. Right posterior tibial
8. Right peroneal
9. Right dorsalis pedis
10. Right arcuate
11. Right dorsal metatarsal
12. Right dorsal digital
13. Right lateral plantar
14. Right medial plantar
15. Right plantar arch
16. Right plantar metatarsal
17. Right plantar digital

Answers to Table 18.6

1. External iliac
2. Internal iliac
3. Right femoral
4. Right popliteal
5. Right dorsalis pedis
6. Right dorsal digital
7. Right medial plantar
8. Right plantar arch
9. Right plantar digital

Answers to Figure 18.7

1. Superior sagittal sinus
2. Inferior sagittal sinus
3. Straight sinus
4. Right transverse (lateral) sinus
5. Right sigmoid sinus
6. Right external jugular
7. Right vertebral
8. Right internal jugular
9. Right cavernous sinus

Answers to Table 18.8

1. Straight sinus
2. Right transverse sinus
3. Right subclavian vein
4. Right internal jugular vein
5. Right brachiocephalic vein
6. Left brachiocephalic vein

Answers to Figure 18.8 (a)

1. Right accessory cephalic
2. Right cephalic
3. Right dorsal venous arch
4. Right dorsal metacarpal
5. Right dorsal digital
6. Right basilic

Answers to Figure 18.8 (b)

1. Right median antebrachial
2. Right palmar digital
3. Right palmar venous plexus

Answers to Figure 18.8 (c)

1. Right ulnar
2. Right deep venous palmar arch
3. Right superficial venous palmar arch
4. Right palmar metacarpal
5. Right common palmar digital
6. Right proper palmar digital
7. Right radial

Answers to Figure 18.8 (d)

1. Right subclavian
2. Right axillary
3. Right cephalic
4. Right brachials
5. Right accessory cephalic
6. Right basilic
7. Right median cubital
8. Right radials
9. Right ulnars
10. Right median antebrachial
11. Right palmar venous plexus

Answers to Table 18.9

1. Right brachiocephalic
2. Right internal jugular
3. Right subclavian
4. Right axillary
5. Right radial
6. Right ulnar
7. Right accessory cephalic
8. Right palmar venous plexus
9. Right dorsal metacarpal
10. Right palmar metacarpal
11. Right common palmar digital

Answers to Figure 18.9

1. Accessory hemiazygos
2. Left intercostal
3. Hemiazygos
4. Left ascending lumbar
5. Left subcostal
6. Right subcostal
7. Right ascending lumbar
8. Azygos

Answers to Table 18.10

1. Right brachiocephalic
2. Azygos
3. Hemiazygos
4. Right ascending lumbar
5. Left subcostal

Answers to Figure 18.10

1. Inferior phrenics
2. Suprarenals
3. Inferior vena cava
4. Left lumbars
5. Left asscending lumbar
6. Left subcostal
7. Right external iliac
8. Right internal iliac
9. Right common iliac
10. Gonadals
11. Renals
12. Hepatics

Answers to Table 18.11

1. Inferior vena cava
2. Right common iliac
3. Left common iliac
4. Right external iliac
5. Left internal iliac

Answers to Figure 18.11 (a) and (b)

1. Right deep femoral
2. Right femoral
3. Right great saphenous
4. Right popliteal
5. Right anterior tibial
6. Right small saphenous
7. Right peroneal
8. Right posterior tibial
9. Right dorsalis pedis
10. Right dorsal venous arch
11. Right dorsal metatarsal
12. Right dorsal digital
13. Right medial plantar
14. Right deep plantar venous arch
15. Right plantar digital
16. Right plantar metatarsal
17. Right lateral plantar

Answers to Table 18.12

1. Right common iliac
2. Right external iliac
3. Right deep femoral
4. Right popliteal
5. Right anterior tibial
6. Right great saphenous
7. Right medial and lateral plantar
8. Right dorsal metatarsal
9. Right plantar metatarsal

Answers to Figure 18.12 (a)

1. Splenic
2. Superior mesenteric
3. Hepatic portal
4. Hepatic

Answers to Figure 18.12 (b)

1. Splenic vein
2. Superior mesenteric vein
3. Hepatic veins
4. Hepatic artery

Answers to Figure 18.13 (a)

1. Right pulmonary artery
2. Right pulmonary vein
3. Pulmonary trunk
4. Left pulmonary artery
5. Left pulmonary vein

Answers to Figure 18.13 (b)

1. Pulmonary trunk
2. Left pulmonary veins
3. Right pulmonary artery

Answers to Figure 18.14 (a)

1. Foramen ovale
2. Ductus venosus
3. Umbilical vein
4. Umbilical arteries
5. Umbilical cord
6. Ductus arteriosus
7. Placenta

Answers to Figure 18.14 (b)

1. Ductus arteriosus
2. Umbilical arteries
3. Umbilical vein
4. Ductus venosus
5. Foramen ovale

Answers to E. Blood Vessel Exercises

1. Coronary artery – Supplies heart
2. Internal iliac veins – Drain the pelvic wall and viscera, external genitals, buttocks, and medial aspect of thigh
3. Lumbar arteries – Supply spinal cord and its meninges and skin of lumbar region
4. Renal artery – Supplies kidney
5. Left gastric artery – Supplies stomach
6. External jugular vein – Drains parotid glands, facial muscles, and scalp
7. Left subclavian artery – Supplies left vertebral artery and vessels of left upper limb
8. Axillary vein – Drains arm and hand
9. Brachiocephalic vein – Drains head, neck, upper limbs, mammary glands, and upper thorax
10. Transverse sinuses – Drain brain
11. Hepatic artery – Supplies liver
12. Inferior mesenteric artery – Supplies large intestine and rectum
13. Suprarenal artery – Supplies adrenal glands
14. Inferior phrenic artery – Supplies inferior surface of diaphragm
15. Great saphenous veins – Drains leg
16. Popliteal vein – Drains anterior and posterior tibials and small saphenous veins
17. Azygos vein – Drains thorax
18. Internal iliac artery – Supplies gluteal muscles, medial side of each thigh, urinary bladder, rectum, prostate gland, uterus, and vagina
19. Internal carotid artery – Supplies brain, eye, side of forehead, and nose
20. Cephalic vein – Drains arm and hand

4. Answers to Laboratory Report Questions:

Answers to Part 1. Multiple Choice

1. (a)
2. (b)
3. (c)
4. (d)
5. (c)
6. (d)
7. (c)
8. (a)
9. (d)
10. (c)
11. (c)
12. (d)
13. (b)
14. (a)
15. (a)
16. (c)
17. (d)
18. (a)
19. (b)
20. (c)

Answers to Part 2. Matching

21. D
22. C
23. B
24. A
25. E
26. J
27. I
28. H
29. F
30. G

Answers to Part 3. Completion

31. Left common carotid
32. Brachial
33. Radial
34. Basilar
35. Internal carotid
36. Phrenic
37. Celiac trunk
38. Gastroepiploic
39. Superior mesenteric
40. Gonadal
41. Inferior phrenic
42. Common iliac
43. Dorsalis pedis
44. Plantar arch
45. Coronary sinus
46. Vertebral
47. Transverse
48. Dorsal venous arch
49. Basilic
50. Median antebrachial
51. Axillary
52. Subclavian
53. Accessory hemiazygos
54. Common iliac
55. Great saphenous
56. Small saphenous
57. Popliteal

19
Cardiovascular Physiology

1. Materials Needed:

Stethoscope
Swabs
70% alcohol
Sterile cotton
Electrocardiograph, polygraph, or kymograph
Tension transducers
EKG electrodes and cables
Electrode cream, jelly, or saline paste
Paper towels
Syphygmomanometer
Pencils
Straight-edge rulers
Cloth
Rubber bands
Live frog
Frog board (constructed out of soft wood, approximately 8" x 4" x 1/4" with 1" diameter hole near one end)
Live turtle
Turtle board
Thread and hook
Probe
Dissecting pins
Krebs-Ringer's solution (contains 250 mg of $CaCl_2$, 420 mg of KCl, and 9000 mg of NaCl per liter)
1:10,000 solution of histamine
1:1000 solution of acetylcholine
1:1000 solution of atropine sulfate
1:1000 solution of epinephrine
Antihistamine solution (made by dissolving one generic antihistamine tablet in about 20 mL of water)
Dissecting instruments and trays
Rubber gloves
Laboratory coat

2. Suggested Audiovisual Materials

Videocassettes

Life Under Pressure (26 min; C; Sd; 1990; FHS)
The Human Body: What Can Go *Wrong?* (six filmstrips on video/cassettes/guide; EI)

Films: 8 mm

Heart in Action: Circulation: The Flow of Blood (both C; Sd; EBEC)

Transparencies: overhead projection

Cardiovascular System — -Unit 6 (16 transparencies; RJB)
Circulatory System; Circulatory System: Heart Pumping Cycle (both GAF)
Heart: Circulatory System (both HSC)
Human Blood Vascular System I (CARO)
Mammalian Circulatory System (K&E)

Computer Software

Cardiovascular System (IBM; PLP)
Dynamics of the Human Circulatory System (IBM; EI)
Understanding Human Physiology: Cardiovascular Function (IBM: PLP)

3. Answers to Illustrations and/or Questions:

Answers to Figure 19.1

1. Sinoatrial (SA) node
2. Atrioventricular (AV) node
3. Atrioventricular (AV) bundle (bundle of His)
4. Bundle branches
5. Conduction myofibers (Purkinje fibers)

4. Answers to Laboratory Report Questions:

Answers to Part 1. Multiple Choice

1. (a)
2. (a)
3. (b)
4. (b)
5. (c)

Answers to Part 2. Completion

6. A cardiac cycle, a heartbeat
7. Isolvolumic contraction
8. Valves
9. Murmurs
10. Radial artery
11. Conduction
12. Electrocardiograph
13. P wave
14. Deflection waves
15. Sphygmomanometer
16. Brachial
17. Korotkoff
18. Pulse pressure
19. 120 mm Hg/80 mm Hg
20. 40 mm Hg

20
Lymphatic System

1. Materials Needed:

Textbook of anatomy and physiology
Charts and models of lymphatic system
Double-injected preserved cat
Dissecting instruments and tray
Rubber gloves
Laboratory coat
Biostat
Prepared slides of:
  spleen (with red and white pulp)
  Thymus gland (with lobules and thymic [Hassal's] corpuscles)

2. Suggested Audiovisual Materials

Videocassettes

AIDS (12 min; C; Sd; 1991; PLP)
AIDS-Changing Lifestyles (15 min; C; Sd; 1991; GA)
AIDS: Everyday Precautions for Health Care Workers (3 parts for laboratory professionals and support service employees; 30 min each; C; Sd; 1990; GA)
AIDS: Facts and Fears, Crisis and Controversy (56 min; C; Sd; 1990; GA)
AIDS, HIV and Seroconversion: What You Should Know (30 min; C; Sd; 1990; GA)
AIDS-Nobody Is Immune (15 min; C; Sd; 1991; PLP)
AIDS: Questions with Answers (15 min; C; Sd; 1991; PLP)
AIDS: On the Trail of a Killer (52 min; C; Sd; 1990; FHS)
AIDS: Our Worst Fears (57 min; C; Sd; 1990; FHS)
AIDS-The Global Impact (15 min; C; Sd; 1990; GA)
AIDS: What Are the Risks? (filmstrip on video; 1991; HRM)
AIDS: What Everyone Needs to Know (19 min; C; Sd; 1990; CHUR/KSU)
Allergy and Immunotherapy (26 min; C; Sd; 1990; FHS)
Bacteria a& Viruses (20 min; C; Sd; 1990; FHS)
Body Defenses Against Disease, 3rd edition (22 min; C; Sd; 1990; GA)
Cell Wars (26 min; C; Sd; 1990; FHS)
How Infection Strikes (20 min; C; Sd; 1990; FHS)
Internal Defenses (26 min; C; Sd; 1990; FHS)
Living with Cancer (Hodgkin's disease} (26 min: C; Sd: 1990; FHS)
Organ Transplants (19 min; C; Sd; I991 ; FHS)
Overcoming Irrational Fear of AIDS (22 min: C; Sd; 1990; KSU)
Ryan White Talks to Kids About AIDS (28 min: C; Sd: 1990: FHS)
Sexual Roulette: AIDS and the Heterosexual (26 min: C; Sd; 1990: FHS)
Stress and Immune Function (26 min; C; Sd: 1990: FHS)
The AIDS Epidemic: Is Anyone Safe? (SO min: C; Sd: 1990: GA)
The Biology of Viruses (16 min: C: Sd: PLP)
T/7e Body Against Diseases (filmstrip on video: 1990: HRM)
The Clinical Story of AIDS: An Interview with Dr. Pau Volberding (28 min; C: Sd:
The Common Cold (28 min; C; Sd; 1990; FHS)

Transplant (Sd; 1990; FHS)
Transplants: The Immune System at Risk (29 min; C; Sd; 1990; PLP)
Vaccines and preventive Medicine (26 min: C: Sd: 1990: FHS)
Viruses, Retroviruses and AIDS: An Interview with Dr. Luc Montagnier (28 min: C: Sd: 1990; CONN)
What is Microbiology? (67 slides on video: cassette/guide: IM)
***Wonder** Drugs* {antibiotics} (106 frames on video/cassette; El)

Films: 16 mm

To Make Man Immune from Disease (20 min; C; Sd; UIFC)

Transparencies: 35 mm

Anaphylactic Hypersensitivity (80 slides/cassette; EI)
Antigen-Antibody Reactions (101 slides/cassette; EI)
Antigens and lmmunogens (58 slides/cassette; EI)
Bacteria: Invisible Friends and Foes (220 slides/3 cassettes; 1988; EI)
Cytotoxic Hypersensitivity (47 slides/cassette; EI
Hyper-Immunoglobulinemias (51 slides/cassette; EI)
Immune Complex Disease (68 slides/cassette; EI)
Immunoglobulin Structure and Function (101 slides/cassette; EI)
Immunologic Deficiency States (115 slides/2 cassettes; EI)
Introduction to Bacteria (20 slides/guide; El)
Introduction to Viruses (15 slides/guide; EI)
Lymphocyte-Mediated Hypersensitivity (63 slides/cassette; EI)
Lymphoid Organs Set (20 slides; CARO)
Mammalian Histology: Blood and Lymph System (20 slides/guide; EI)
Mounting Immune Responses (101 slides/cassette; EI)
Parasitic Organisms (20 slides; EI)
The Complement Systems (68 slides/cassette; EI)
The Immune Response (10 slides/cassette/guide; EI)
Transplantation Immunology (77 slides in tray/cassettes/guide; EI)
Viruses: The Mysterious Enemy(147 slides/2 cassettes/guide; EI)
Visual Approach to Histology: Lymphatic System (18 slides; FAD)
What Is Microbiology? (67 slides; cassette/guide; IM)

Transparencies: overhead projection

Disease and Health (12 overheads, 4 duplicating masters; CONN)
Human Lymphatic System (CARO)

Computer Software

Allergist (IBM; PLP)
Body Defenses (IBM; PLP)
Choices: AIDS (IBM; PLP)
Disease, Immunity and Health (IBM, Macintosh; QUEUE)
Graphic Human Anatomy and Physiology Tutor: Lymphatic System (IBM; PLP)
Host Non-specific Defense Systems Against Infectious Diseases (MAC)
Identification and Alleviation of Allergies (MAC)
Life Sciences Lab Simulator /Agents of Infection (IBM; PLP)
Life Sciences Lab Simulator/Body Defenses (IBM; PLP)

Medical Microbiology Review (IBM; EI)
Microbe (CARO)
Pathology: Diseases and Defenses (IBM; CARO)
The Immune Defense System (MAC)
Understanding AIDS (IBM, Macintosh; CARO/PLP/GA)
Understanding AIDS (IBM; PLP)
Understanding the Human Fight to Stay Healthy (IBM, Macintosh; QUEUE)
Communicable Disease: The Traveling Germ (CARO)
Immunization: A Shot in Time (CARO)
Transplants: The Immune System at Risk (PLP)
Parasitic Organisms (EIL)

3. Answers to Illustrations and/or Questions:

Answers to Figure 20.1

1. Axillary node
2. Cisterna chyli
3. Iliac node
4. Inguinal node
5. Intestinal node
6. Thoracic duct
7. Right subclavian vein
8. Right lymphatic duct
9. Cervical node
10. Submandibular node

Answers to Figure 20.3

1. Capsule
2. Trabecula
3. Cortex
4. Medulla
5. thymic (Hassall's) corpuscle

Answers to Figure 20.4

1. Lymphatic follicle
2. Germinal center
3. Medullary cord
4. Trabecula
5. Efferent lymphatic vessel
6. Hilus
7. Capsule
8. Afferent lymphatic vessel

Answers to Figure 20.5

1. Capsule
2. Red pulp
3. Trabecula
4. Central artery
5. White pulp

4. Answers to Laboratory Report Questions:

Answers to Part 1. Multiple Choice

1. (d)
2. (c)
3. (d)
4. (d)
5. (d)
6. (d)
7. (a)

Answers to Part 1. Completion

8. Lymph nodes
9. Valves
10. Right lymphatic duct
11. Efferent
12. Plasma cells
13. Lymphangiography
14. Carcinomas
15. Spleen
16. Thoracic (left lymphatic)
17. Follicles
18. Palatine
19. Thymus gland
20. Cistern chyli
21. MALT (mucosa-associated lymphoid tissue)
22. Parenchyma

21
Respiratory System

1. Materials Needed:

Textbook of anatomy and physiology
Compound microscope
Dissecting microscope
Lens paper
Torso
Charts, models, slides, and preserved specimens of human respiratory organs
Preserved sheep pluck
Live frog
Dissecting instruments and tray
Rubber gloves
Laboratory coat
Biostat
Pithing needle
Pins
Model lung (bell jar demonstrator)
Collins respirometer with disposable mouthpieces and noseclip
Collins VC timed interval ruler
Prepared slides of:
    Pseudostratified ciliated columnar epithelium from trachea
    Normal lung tissue
    Emphysematous tissue
    Cancerous lung tissue
Pulmometer (handheld respirometer) kit
Ringer's solution
70% alcohol
Sterile cotton
Noseclip
Pneumograph
Paper bags
Stethoscope
Sphygmomanometer
Measuring tape
Chest calipers
Vital capacity apparatus
Exercise cycle or 20-in platform
Pyrex® test tubes and test tube rack
Marking pencil
Straws
Calcium hydroxide [$Ca(OH)_2$]
Stop watch

2. Suggested Audiovisual Materials

Videocassettes

Asthma (19 min; 1990; FHS)
Breath of Life (26 min; 1990; FHS)
Cystic Fibrosis (26 min; 1991; FHS)
Partners for Life: The Human Heart and Lungs (2 filmstrips on video with guide; EI)
Respiration (29 min; 1990; IM)
Respiration: Energy for Life (47 min; 1990; IM/EI/GA)
The Common Cold (28 min; 1990; FHS)
The Human Body: Respiratory System (14 min; 1993; COR)
Up in Smoke: How Smoking Affects Your Health (38 min; 1990; GA)

Films: 16 mm

Basic Anatomy and physiology of the Mammal: The Respiratory System (9 min; UIFC)
Breathing and Respiration (19 min; PHC)
Carbon Monoxide Poisoning (3 min; IF)
Chemical Balance Through Respiration (29 min; NFM)
CPR Quiz: Basic Life Support (21 min; TLV)
CPR Trainer (21 min; TLV)
Gas Exchange in the Respiratory System (4 min; HC)
Living with Cystic Fibrosis (36 min; KSU)
Lungs and Pressure-Volume Relationships (20 min; TNF)
Mechanics of Breathing (20 min; TNF)
Principles of Artificial Respiration (29 min; TNF)
Principles of Respiratory Mechanics (two parts, 22 min each; AMA)
The Embattled Cell [lung cancer] (ACS)
The Nose (11 min; EBEC)

Films: 8 mm

Biology: Respiratory System: Breathing (EBF)
Breathing Movement (H&B)

Transparencies: 35 mm

Biology: Respiratory System: Breathing (EBF)
Mammalian Histology: Respiratory, Circulatory, & Urinary Systems (20 slides/guide; EI)
Respiration (71 slides; EI)
Respiratory System and Its Function (20 slides; EIL)
Visual Approach to Histology: Respiratory System (11 slides; FAD)

Transparencies: overhead projection

Respiratory System (HSC)
Respiratory System: Structure; Air Expired, Inspired (GAF)
Respiratory System — Unit 7 (C, 10 transparencies: RJB)

Computer Software

Body Language: Respiratory System (IBM, Macintosh; PLP)
Circulation and Respiration (IBM, Macintosh; QUEUE)
Dynamics of the Human Respiratory System (IBM; EI)
Graphic Human Anatomy & Physiology Tutor: Respiratory System (IBM; PLP)
Understanding Human Physiology: Exercise Physiology (IBM; PLP)

3. Answers to Illustrations and/or Questions:

Answers to Figure 21.1

1. Pharynx
2. Bronchi
3. Nasal cavity
4. Larynx
5. Trachea
6. Lungs

Answers to Figure 21.1

1. Internal naris
2. Superior nasal concha (turbinate)
3. Superior meatus
4. Middle nasal concha (turbinate)
5. Middle meatus
6. Inferior nasal concha (turbinate)
7. Nasal cavity
8. Inferior meatus
9. Vestibule
10. Hard palate
11. Oral cavity
12. Soft palate
13. Thyroid cartilage (Adam's apple)
14. Ventricular fold (false vocal cord)
15. Vocal fold (true vocal cord)
16. Laryngopharynx
17. Palatine tonsil
18. Oropharynx
19. Nasopharynx
20. Pharyngeal tonsil

Answers to Figure 21.4 (a) and (b)

1. Epiglottis
2. Corniculate cartilage
3. Arytenoid cartilage
4. Cricoid cartilage
5. Thyroid cartilage (Adam's apple)

Answers to Figure 21.4 (c)

1. Ventricular fold (false focal fold)
2. Thyroid cartilage
3. Vocal fold (true vocal fold)
4. Cricoid cartilage
5. Arytenoid cartilage
6. Corniculate cartilage
7. Cuneiform cartilage
8. Epiglottis

Answers to Figure 21.5

1. Ventricular folds (false vocal folds)
2. Vocal folds (true vocal folds)
3. Rima glottidis

Answers to Figure 21.6

1. Right primary bronchus
2. Right secondary (lobar) bronchi
3. Left tertiary (segmental) bronchi
4. Left bronchioles
5. Left terminal bronchioles

Answers to Figure 21.7

1. Ciliated columnar cell
2. Goblet cell
3. Cilia
4. Basal cell

Answers to Figure 21.8 (a) and (c)

1. Superior lobe
2. Horizontal fissure
3. Middle lobe
4. Oblique fissure of right lung
5. Cardiac notch
6. Oblique fissure of left lung
7. Inferior lobe
8. Terminal bronchiole
9. Pulmonary arteriole
10. Lymphatic vessel
11. Respiratory bronchiole
12. Alveolar ducts
13. Alveolar sac
14. Alveoli
15. Pulmonary venule

Answers to Figure 21.9

1. Capillary basement membrane
2. Capillary endothelium
3. Type II alveolar (septal) cell
4. Alveolar-capillary (respiratory) membrane
5. Type I alveolar (squamous pulmonary epithelial) cell
6. Epithelial basement membrane
7. Alveolar macrophage (dust cell)

Answers to Figure 21.13

Stopcock = rima glottidis
Glass tube (upper) = trachea
Glass tube (lower) = primary bronchus
Balloon = lung
Pressure in lungs = alveolar pressure
Pressure between pleural layers = intrapleural pressure
Glass jar = chest wall
Rubber membrane = diaphragm

4. Answers to Laboratory Report Questions:

Answers to Part 1. Multiple Choice

1. (b)
2. (c)
3. (c)
4. (c)
5. (d)
6. (d)
7. (c)
8. (b)
9. (d)
10. (b)

Answers to Part 2. Completion

11. Filtered
12. Cleft palate
13. Epiglottis
14. Larynx
15. Pseudostratified ciliated columnar epithelium
16. Intubation
17. Bronchogram
18. Terminal bronchioles
19. Nasal septum
20. External nares
21. Speech sounds
22. Pleurisy
23. Vestibule
24. Meatuses
25. Oropharynx
26. Lobules
27. Alveolus
28. Cricoid
29. Base
30. Alveolar macrophage
31. Costal
32. Hilus
33. Upper
34. Dorsum nasi
35. Arytenoid
36. Bronchopulmonary

Answers to Part 3. Matching

37. D
38. E
39. B
40. A
41. C
42. F

Answers to Part 4. Matching

43. A
44. B
45. B
46. A
47. A

Answers to Part 5. Matching

48. A
49. E
50. B
51. C
52. D
53. D
54. B, C
55. B

22
Digestive System

1. Materials Needed:

Textbook of anatomy and physiology
Compound microscope
Lens paper
Prepared slides of:
- Parotid salivary gland
- Submandibular salivary gland
- Sublingual salivary gland
- Transverse section of esophagus
- Transverse section of stomach
- Liver lobules
- Transverse section of small intestine
- Villi of small intestine
- Transverse section of large intestine

Torso
Charts, models, slides, and preserved specimens of human digestive organs
Double-injected preserved cats
Dissecting instruments and trays
Rubber gloves
Laboratory coat
Biostat
Bunsen burner
Mirrors
Tongue depressors
Crackers
Cup
Stethoscope
Alcohol swabs
White rat already sacrificed
Kymograph or polygraph and accessory apparatus
Amylase powder (small bottle of commercial amylase powder)
Benedict's solution (commercial bottle of approximately 1000
serves 24 students)
Starch solution
Lugol's solution
Spot plates
Straight glass rods
L-shaped glass tubing
Rubber hose
Ice cubes
Thread
pH solutions of 4.0, 7.0 and 9.0
Pyrex® test tubes, 25 per group of 4 students
Beakers (500-m] and 1000-mL sizes),1 of each size per group of 4 students
Test tube racks
Test tube holders

Pancreatin solution (prepared in sodium carbonate; 300 mL serves 24 students)
Litmus cream
Thermometers
Medicine droppers
Pipettes (1-mL and 5-mL capacity)
Graduated cylinders (10-mL capacity)
Bile solution (150 mL serves 24 students)
Vegetable oil
Sudan B dye solution
Pepsin solution (1000 mL serves 24 students)
Fibrin
0.8% HCl solution (500 mL serves 24 students)
0.5% NaOH solution (200 mL serves 24 students)
Hydrion pH paper strips
Hot plates
Air supply
Locke's solution (contains 200 mg of $CaCl_2$, 200 mg of KCl, 200 mg of $NaHC0_3$, 9500 mg of NaCl, and 1000 mg of glucose per liter adjusted to pH 7.8)
1:50,000 solution of norepinephrine
1:1,000 solution of acetylcholine
1:50,000 solution of atropine
$O(Ca)_e$ solution (contains 200 mg of KCl, 200 mg of $NaHC0_3$, 9500 mg of NaCl, and 1000 mg of glucose per liter adjusted to pH 7.8)

2. Suggested Audiovisual Materials

Videocassettes

Alcohol: The Social Drug, the Personal Problem (50 min; C; Sd; 1990; GA)
Animal Nutrition (29 min; C; Sd; 1990; IM)
Anorexia and Bulimia (19 min; C; Sd; 1990; FHS)
Breakdown (26 min; C; Sd; 1990; FHS)
Cystic Fibrosis (26 min; C; Sd; 1991; FHS)
Dangerous Dieting: The Wrong Way to Lose Weight (filmstrip on video; 1990; HRM)
Diet: Health and Disease (filmstrip on video; 1990; HRM)
Eating-Out of Control (30 min; C; Sd; 1990; PLP)
Eating to Live (26 min; C; Sd; 1990; FHS)
Food and Cancer Prevention (30+ min; C; Sd; 1990; PLP)
Hard Facts about Drugs: Alcohol, Marijuana, Cocaine and Crack (22 min; C; Sd; 1990; GA)
The Addicted Brain (26 min; C; Sd; 1990; FHS)
The Danger Zone: Substance Abuse (17 min; C; Sd; 1990; PLP)
Wasting A way: Understanding Anorexia Nervosa and Bulimia (40 min: C; Sd; 1991; GA)

Films: 16 mm

Alimentary Tract (11 min; EBEC)
Basic Anatomy and Physiology of the Mammal: The Digestive System (7 min; UIFC)
Digestion: Mechanics (18 min; UWF)
Good Sense About Your Stomach (14 min: TLV)
Intravenous Hyper-Alimentation Technique (21 min; ABB/KSU)

The Liver (15 min; IFB)

Films: 8 mm

Digestion in the Small Intestine (C; Si; H&B)
Swallowing (C; Si; H&B)
The Digestive Tract (C; Si; EFL)
The Stomach in Action (C; Si; H&B)

Transparencies: 35 mm

Digestive System (slides 47-82; McG)
Digestive System and Its Function (20 slides; EUCONN)
Endoscopy Medical Slide Series (115 slides; CARO)
Mammalian Histology: Digestive System-Mouth to Esophagus (20 slides; EI)
Mammalian Histology: Digestive System — Stomach, Intestine & Major Glands (20 slides; EI)
Stomach, Kidneys, Bladder, ureters, Large Intestine (TSED)
Teeth And Their Function (20 slides; El)
The Digestive System: The Digestive Tube Set (30 slides; CARO)
The Digestive System The Glands of Digestion Set (I6 slides; CARO)
The Digestive System: The Oral Cavity Set (20 slides; CARO)
Visual Approach to Histology: Digestive System (48 slides: FAD)

Transparencies: overhead projection

Digestive System (HSC)
Digestive System-Unit 8 (C; 11 transparencies; RJB)
Digestive System: Overview; Mouth; Structure of Small Intestine; Teeth (all GAF)
Peptide Bond Formation: Some Amino Acids; Synthesis and Digestion of Disaccharides; Synthesis and Digestion of Fats (all K&E)
Structure of a Tooth (TSED)
The Table of Foods; Daily Calorie Requirement; Sugar Economy of the Body; The Digestion of Carbohydrates; The Buildup and Breakdown of Carbohydrates; The Digestion of Fats; The Digestion of Albumin; Human Digestion; Sound Teeth, Carries and Dental Treatment; Human Digestive organs; Human Digestive System. 2-6 (all CARO)

Computer Software

Body Language: Digestive System (IBM, Macintosh; PLP)
Digestion and Excretion (IBM, Macintosh; QUEUE)
Digestive System (IBM; PLP)
Dynamics of the Human Digestive System (IBM; El)
Dynamics of the Human Teeth (IBM; EI)
Graphic Human Anatomy and Physiology Tutor: Digestive System (IBM; PLP)

3. Answers to Illustrations and/or Questions:

Answers to Figure 22.1

1. Liver
2. Gallbladder
3. Transverse colon
4. Ascending colon
5. Cecum
6. Appendix
7. Stomach
8. Spleen
9. Pancreas
10. Duodenum
11. Jejunum
12. Ileum
13. Descending colon
14. Sigmoid colon
15. Rectum
16. Anus

Answers to Figure 22.2

1. Superior labium
2. Superior labial frenulum
3. Gingivae
4. Palatoglossal arch
5. Palatopharyngeal arch
6. Fauces
7. Palatine tonsil
8. Tongue
9. Lingual frenulum
10. Inferior labial frenulum
11. Inferior labium
12. Vestibule
13. Cheek
14. Uvula
15. Soft palate
16. Hard palate

Answers to Figure 22.3

1. Parotid gland
2. Parotid (Stensen's) duct
3. Opening of parotid (Stensen's) duct
4. Lesser sublingual (Rivinus') duct
5. Sublingual gland
6. Submandibular (Wharton's) duct
7. Submandibular gland

Answers to Figure 22.5

1. Enamel
2. Dentin
3. Gingiva
4. Pulp cavity
5. Pulp
6. Cementum
7. Root canal
8. Peridontal ligament
9. Apical foramen
10. Root
11. Neck
12. Crown

Answers to Figure 22.6 (a) and (b)

1. Second molar
2. First molar
3. Cuspid (canine)
4. Lateral incisor
5. Central incisor
6. Third molar (wisdom tooth)
7. Second premolar (bicuspid)
8. First premolar (bicuspid)

Answers to Figure 22.7

1. Mucosa
2. Submucosa
3. Muscularis
4. Adventitia

Answers to Figure 22.8 (a) and (b)

1. Cardia
2. Body
3. Lesser curvature
4. Pylorus
5. Pyloric sphincter (valve)
6. Pyloric canal
7. Pyloric antrum
8. Greater curvature
9. Fundus

Answers to Figure 22.9 (a)

1. Gastric pit
2. Mucosa
3. Submucosa
4. Muscularis
5. Serosa

Answers to Figure 22.10

1. Falciform ligament
2. Left hepatic duct
3. Left lobe of liver
4. Common hepatic duct
5. Common bile duct
6. Accessory pancreatic duct (duct of Santorini)
7. Tail of pancreas
8. Body of pancreas
9. Head of pancreas
10. Pancreatic duct (duct of Wirsung)
11. Hepatopancreatic ampulla (ampulla of Vater)
12. Duodenal papilla
13. Gallbladder
14. Cystic duct
15. Right hepatic duct
16. Right lobe of liver

Answers to Figure 22.14

1. Transverse colon
2. Right colic (hepatic) flexure
3. Ascending colon
4. Ileocecal sphincter (valve)
5. Cecum
6. Vermiform appendix
7. Descending colon
8. Sigmoid colon
9. Anal canal
10. Anus

4. Answers to Laboratory Report Questions:

Answers to Part 1. Multiple Choice

1. (c)
2. (a)
3. (c)
4. (a)
5. (b)
6. (d)
7. (b)
8. (c)
9. (a)
10. (b)
11. (a)
12. (d)
13. (d)
14. (b)
15. (d)
16. (b)
17. (c)
18. (a)
19. (d)

Answers to Part 2. Completion

20. Peritonitis
21. Ileocecal sphincter (valve)
22. Duodenum
23. Cardia
24. Tongue
25. Greater curvature
26. Microvilli
27. Sublingual
28. Jejunum
29. Anal canal
30. Salivary amylase
31. Vermilion
32. Circumvallate
33. Pulp cavity
34. Premolars (bicuspids)
35. Esophagus
36. Pylorus
37. Acini
38. Liver
39. Cystic
40. Gallbladder
41. Duodenal
42. Mesocolon
43. Rectum
44. Labial frenulum
45. Dentin
46. Peridontal ligament
47. Sigmoid
48. Palatopharyngeal
49. Central incisors
50. Cecum
51. Bolus
52. Chief (zymogenic) cells

Answers to Part 3. Matching

53. E
54. D
55. A
56. B
57. C

23
Urinary System

1. Materials Needed:

Textbook of anatomy and physiology
Dissecting instruments and trays
Compound microscope
Lens paper
Prepared slides of:
 Various components of a nephron and associated structures (glomerular)
 [Bowman's] capsule, glomerulus, proximal convoluted tubules, distal convoluted tubules, and collecting tubules
 Ureter
 Urinary bladder
Torso
Charts, models, slides, and preserved specimens of human urinary system organs
Sterile containers for urine collection
Wooden sticks or swabs
Chemistrips® or similar strips
Urinometers
Benedict's solution
Hot plates
Thermometers
Beakers, 500-m] and 1000-mL sizes (one of each size per lab)
Pyrex® test tubes, 10 per 4 students
Test tube racks
Clinitest® regent tablets
Medicine dropper
pH Paper
Double-injected preserved cats
Preserved sheep (or pork) kidneys
Rubber gloves
Laboratory coat
Biostat
Live goldfish
Table-top centrifuge
Funnels
Filter papers
Acetic acid- 10%
Ablutest' regent tablets
Acetest® tablets
Sodium nitroprusside crystals and spatula
Icotest® tablets and kits
Sedistain
Phenol red (0.05 M)
Penicillin G (1 M)
Trichlorophenol (1 mM) or 2,4 dini-trophenol (0.2 mM)
Potassium chromatic solution (20%) with dropper

Silver nitrate solution (2.9%) with dropper
Slides and cover slips
Depression slides
Medicine droppers
Graduated cylinders, 10-mL capacity (1 per student)
Pipettes, l-mL and 5-mL capacity (1 of each size per student)
China marking pencils
Centrifuge tubes (1 per student)

2. Suggested Audiovisual Materials

Videocassettes

Kidney Disease (26 min; 1992; FHS)
The Human Body: Excretory System (12 min; 1993; COR)
The Mammalian Kidney (20 min; EI)
The Mammalian Kidney (72 slides on video with guide; EI)
Water! (26 min; 1990; FHS/CARO)

Films: 16 mm

Elimination (11 min; UWF)
Kidney Function in Disease (46 min; LILLY)
Kidney Function in Health (38 min; LILLY)
Kidneys, Ureters, and Bladders (11 min; IU)
The Vertebrate Kidney (24 min; PSU)

Transparencies: 35 mm

Execretory System: Derail of the Human Kidney Tubule (GAF)
Excretory System: Human Skin (GAF)
Mammalian Histology: Respiratory, Circulatory Urinary System (20 slides/guide; EI)
Stomach. Kidneys. Bladder; Urethra. Large Intestine (TSED)
The Mammalian Kidney (72 slides/cassette/guide; EI)
The Urinary System Set (CARO)
Urinary System —-Unit 9 (7 slides; RJB)
Urine Under The Microscope Medical Slide Series (147 slides; CARO)

Transparencies: overhead projection

Functions and Excretions of the Kidneys (CARO)
Human Urinary System (CARO)

Computer Software

Body Language: Urinary and Reproductive Systems (IBM, Macintosh; PLP)
Digestion and Excretion (IBM, Macintosh; QUEUE)
Dynamics of the Human Urinary System (IBM; EI)
Graphic Human Anatomy and Physiology Tutor: Urinary System (IBM; PLP)
Urinary System (IBM; PLP)

3. Answers to Illustrations and/or Questions:

Answers to Figure 23.1

1. Renal artery
2. Renal vein
3. Kidney
4. Ureter
5. Urinary bladder
6. Urethra

Answers to Figure 23.2 (a) and (b)

1. Renal capsule
2. Renal cortex
3. Renal pyramid in renal medulla
4. Renal column
5. Renal papilla
6. Minor calyx
7. Major calyx
8. Renal pelvis

Answers to Figure 23.4 (a) and (b)

1. Collecting duct
2. Distal convoluted tubule
3. Proximal convoluted tubule
4. Glomerulus
5. Ascending limb of the loop of Henle
6. Descending limb of the loop of Henle
7. Glomerular (Bowman's) capsule
8. Papillary duct
9. Capsular space

Answers to Figure 23.7

1. Segmental arteries
2. Interlobar arteries
3. Arcuate arteries
4. Interlobular arteries
5. Afferent arteriole
6. Glomerulus
7. Efferent arteriole
8. Interlobular veins
9. Arcuate veins
10. Interlobar veins
11. Segmental veins

Answers to Figure 23.8

1. Mucosa
2. Transitional epithelium of mucosa
3. Lamina propria of mucosa
4. Muscularis
5. Adventitia

Answers to Figure 23.9

1. Ureters
2. Uretral openings
3. Internal urethral sphincter
4. External urethral sphincter
5. Urethra
6. External urethral opening

Answers to Figure 23.10

1. Mucosa
2. Muscularis

4. Answers to Laboratory Report Questions:

Answers to Part 1. Multiple Choice

1. (d)
2. (a)
3. (b)
4. (a)
5. (d)
6. (a)
7. (c)
8. (b)
9. (b)
10. (a)
11. (d)
12. (d)
13. (b)
14. (c)
15. (d)
16. (b)
17. (d)
18. (c)
19. (a)
20. (a)
21. (b)

Answers to Part 2. Completion

22. Digestive
23. Glomerular (Bowman's) capsule
24. Glomerulus
25. Renal artery
26. Renal plexus
27. Micturition
28. Urethra
29. Papillae
30. Column
31. Major calyces
32. Podocytes
33. Collecting ducts
34. Vasa recti
35. Afferent arterioles
36. Hematuria
37. Calculi (stones)
38. Casts
39. Lower
40. Specific gravity

24
pH and Acid-Base Balance

1. Materials Needed:

Textbook of anatomy and physiology
Forceps
Red and blue litmus paper
100 mL beakers and 250 mL beakers
Milk of magnesia
Vinegar
Coffee
Carbonated soft drink
Orange juice
Distilled water
Baking soda
Lemon juice
Wide-range and narrow-range pH paper
pH meter
Wash bottles
Dropper bottles of 0.05 M HCl
pH 7 buffer solution
Dropper bottles of 0.05 M NaOH
Dropper bottles of 0.01 normal NaOH
Phenol red
straws

2. Suggested Audiovisual Materials

Videocassettes

Buffers (64 slides on video/cassette/guide: EI)
Water! (26 min; C; Sd; 1990; FHS)

Films: 16 mm

Dynamics of Fluid Exchange (30 min; BW: Sd: ACCI)

Transparencies: 35 mm

Buffers (64 slides/cassette/guide; EI/BM/CARO)
Homeostasis: Maintaining the Stability of Life Set (I50 slides with cassettes; SM/CARO)
pH, Osmosis and Diffusion Set (30 slides: CARO)

3. Answers to Illustrations and/or Questions:

(none)

4. Answers to Laboratory Report Questions:

Answers to Part 1. Multiple Choice

1. (b)
2. (d)
3. (c)
4. (b)
5. (c)
6. (a)
7. (d)

Answers to Part 2. Completion

8. Hydroxide
9. Ten
10. Base (alkaline)
11. 7.35 - 7.45
12. Cellular metabolism
13. Acid
14. Increase
15. Decrease
16. Alkalosis
17. Bicarbonate (HCO_3^-)
18. Acidosis
19. Respiratory
20. Hyperventilation

25
Reproductive Systems

1. Materials Needed:

Textbook of anatomy and physiology
Compound microscope
Lens paper
Prepared slides of:
  Testes showing seminiferous tubules
  Ductus epididymis
  Ductus (vas) deferens
  Ovary
  Uterine (Fallopian) tube
  Uterine endometrium showing menstrual, preovulatory, and postovulatory phases of menstrual cycle
  Mammary gland alveoli
Charts and models of reproductive organs
Double-injected preserved cats
Preserved uterus of pregnant pig containing fetus
Dissecting instruments and trays
Rubber gloves
Laboratory coat
Biostat

2. Suggested Audiovisual Materials

Videocassettes

A Woman's Body (49 min; 1990; FHS)
Coming Together (26 min; 1990; FHS)
Gonorrhea/Chlamydia (7 min; 1991; PLP)
Herpes (10 min; 1991; PLP)
Homosexuality (26 min; 1990; FHS)
Human Sexuality and the Life Cycle (filmstrip on video with guide; EI)
Love and Sex (52 min; 1990; FHS)
Meiosis: The Key to Genetic Diversity, (26 min; 1992; HRM/CARO)
Mitosis and Meiosis (45 min: 1990; IM)
Mitosis and Meiosis: How Cells Divide (1990; GA)
Not a Game: Sexually Transmitted Diseases (25 min; 1990; KSU)
One Out of Eleven: Women and Breast Cancer (26 min; 1992; KSU)
Partners With Your Doctor [breast self-examination] (7 min; CARO)
Reproduction and Diversity (25 min: 1990: FHS)
Sex Hormones and Sexual Destiny (26 min; 1990; FHS)
Sexually Transmitted Diseases (19 min: 1990; FHS/PLP)
Sexually Transmitted Diseases: Causes. Prevention and Cure (55 min; 1990; GA)
Sexually Transmitted Skin Diseases (6 min; I991 ; PLP)
Shares in the Future (26 min: 1990; FHS)
Syphilis (7 min; 1991; PLP)
The Human Body: Reproductive System (18 min; 1993; COR)

Vaginitis (8 min; 1991 ; PLP)
What You Don't Know CAN Kill You: Sexually Transmitted Diseases and AIDS (54 min; 1990; GA)
Woman and Man (52 min; 1990; FHS)

Films: 16 mm

About Conception and Contraception (11 min; C; Sd; PE)
Basic Anatomy and Physiology of the Mammal: The Reproductive System (7 min; UIFC)
Breast: Self-Examination (16 min; C; Sd; ACS)
Meiosis (25 min; C; Sd; UIFC)
Meiosis: Sex Cell Formation (16 min; C; Sd; EBEC)
Ovulation (15 min; C; Sd; UIFC)
The Birth Control Movie (24 min; C; Sd; PE)
The Inguinal Canal and Scrotal Contents (25 min; TNF)
VD-A Plague On Our House (35 min; C; Sd; NBC)
Where Spermatozoa Are Formed (9 min; C; Sd: UIFC)

Transparencies: 35 mm

Breast Self Exam (20 slides with cassette and extensive guide; EI)
GLS/Cytogenetics, Unit 5: Gametogenesis and Meiosis (EI)
Histology of the Reproductive System (EI)
Hormones and Reproduction (H&R)
Human Development (20 slides with guide: EI/CONN)
Human *Reproduction* (20 slides with guide: El)
Human Reproduction (GA)
Human Sexuality and the Life Cycle (224 slides with 3 cassettes and guide: El)
Medical Photomicrographs: Obstetrics and Gynecology (100 slides with guide; EI)
Meiosis (74 slides; BM)
Reproductive System and Its Function (20 slides; EI)
Sex is Not a Dirty Word (H&R)
The Female Reproductive System Set (20 slides; CARO)
The Male Reproductive System Set (20 slides; CARO)
The Nature of Human Sexuality (H&R)
Venereal Disease (H&R)
Visual Approach to Histology: Female Reproductive System (22 slides; FAD)
Visual Approach to Histology: Male Reproductive System (15 slides; FAD)

Transparencies: overhead projection

Pregnancy; Human Male Genital Organs; Hormonal Control of Male Glandular Functions; Human Female Genital Organs; Hormonal Control of Female Glandular Functions: The Menstrual Cycle; Birth; Multiple Births; Birth Control and Contraceptives; Sterilization and Castration; Venereal Diseases (all CARO)
Reproductive System -Unit 11 (11 transparencies; RJB)

Computer Software

Body Language: Urinary and Reproductive Systems {anatomy} (IBM, Mac; PLP)
Contraception (IBM, Mac; EI)
Dynamics of the Human Reproductive System (IBM; El)
Graphic Human Anatomy and Physiology Tutor: Reproductive System (IBM; PLP)
Reproduction, Growth, and Development (IBM, Macintosh; QUEUE)

Reproductive Systems (IBM: PLP)
Sexually Transmitted Diseases (IBM. Macintosh; PLP)
The Pap Test (IBM; PLP)
The Reproductive Systems (IBM; PLP)
Venereal Disease (IBM, Mac: El)

3. Answers to Illustrations and/or Questions:

Answers to Figure 25.1

1. Rete testis
2. Straight tubule
3. Seminiferous tubule
4. Lobule
5. Tunica albuginea
6. Ductus epididymis
7. Ductus (vas) deferens
8. Efferent ducts

Answers to Figure 25.2 (a)

1. Sperm cell
2. Spermatid
3. Secondary spermatocyte
4. Primary spermatocyte
5. Sustentacular (Sertoli) cell
6. Spermatogonium
7. Interstitial endocrinocyte (interstitial cell of Leydig)

Answers to Figure 25.2 (b)

1. Sperm cell
2. Spermatid
3. Secondary spermatocyte
4. Primary spermatocyte
5. Spermatogonium
6. Interstitial endocrinocyte (interstitial cell of Leydig)

Answers to Figure 25.3

1. Acrosome
2. Nucleus
3. Mitochondria
4. Tail
5. Midpiece
6. Head

Answers to Figure 25.6

1. Ductus (vas) deferens
2. Seminal vesicle
3. Ejaculatory duct
4. Bulbourethral (Cowper's) gland
5. Prostate gland
6. Urinary bladder
7. Ureter

Answers to Figure 25.7

1. Bulb of the penis
2. Crus of the penis
3. Corpora cavernosa penis
4. Corpus spongiosum penis
5. Corona
6. Glans penis
7. Prepuce
8. External urethral orifice

Answers to Figure 25.8

1. Ductus (vas) deferens
2. Spongy (penile) urethra
3. Penis
4. Epididymis
5. Corona of penis
6. Glans penis
7. Prepuce
8. External urethral orifice
9. Testis
10. Scrotum
11. Membranous urethra
12. Bulbourethral (Cowper's) gland
13. Prostatic urethra
14. Prostate gland
15. Ejaculatory duct
16. Seminal vesicle

Answers to Figure 25.9 (a)

1. Fundus of uterus
2. Uterine (Fallopian) tube
3. Mesovarium
4. Suspensory ligament
5. Fimbriae
6. Ovary
7. Ovarian ligament
8. Broad ligament
9. Body of uterus
10. Internal os
11. Uterosacral ligament
12. External os
13. Vagina
14. cervical canal
15. Cervix
16. Isthmus
17. Uterine cavity
18. Infundibulum

Answers to Figure 25.9 (b)

1. Fundus of uterus
2. Uterine (Fallopian) tube
3. Fimbriae
4. Mesovarium
5. Ovary
6. Ovarian ligament
7. Body of uterus
8. Cervix
9. External os
10. Cervical canal
11. Uterine cavity

Answers to Figure 25.10

1. Primordial follicle
2. Primary (preantral) follicle
3. Secondary (antral) follicle
4. Tunica albuginea
5. germinal epithelium
6. Ovarian medulla
7. Mature (Graafian) follicle
8. Ovarian cortex
9. Mature corpus luteum
10. Corpus albicans

Answers to Figure 25.13

1. Mons pubis
2. Labia majora (spread)
3. Labia minora (spread) exposing vestibule
4. Prepuce
5. Clitoris
6. External urethral orifice
7. Vaginal orifice (dilated)
8. Hymen

Answers to Figure 25.14 (a) and (b)

1. Alveolus
2. Secondary tubules
3. Mammary duct
4. Lactiferous sinus
5. Lactiferous duct
6. Lobules
7. Areola
8. Nipple

Answers to Figure 25.16

1. Ovary
2. Uterine (Fallopian) tube
3. Fimbriae
4. Uterus
5. Round ligament
6. Cervix of uterus
7. Clitoris
8. Vagina
9. Labium minor
10. Labium major
11. Fornix
12. Uterosacral ligament

4. Answers to Laboratory Report Questions:

Answers to Part 1. Multiple Choice

1. (b)
2. (c)
3. (b)
4. (d)
5. (a)
6. (c)
7. (a)
8. (d)
9. (c)
10. (d)
11. (a)
12. (c)
13. (c)
14. (a)
15. (a)
16. (a)
17. (c)
18. (a)
19. (c)

Answers to Part 2. Completion

20. Ovulation
21. Cervix
22. Alveoli
23. Glans
24. Prepuce (foreskin)
25. Areola
26. Infundibulum
27. Head
28. Ductus (vas) deferens
29. Corpus spongiosum penis
30. Corpus luteum
31. Fundus
32. Broad
33. Vagina
34. Labia majora
35. Clitoris
36. Hymen
37. Mammary ducts
38. Germinal epithelium
39. Preovulatory
40. Functionalis
41. Spermatogonia
42. Corpus luteum
43. Gonadotropin releasing hormone (GnRH)
44. Ovulation

26
Development

1. Materials Needed:

Textbook of anatomy and physiology
Charts and models of developmental sequences
Prepared microscopic slides of embryonic development of the sea urchin

2. Suggested Audiovisual Materials

Videocassettes

A New Life (26 min; 1990; FHS/CARO)
Contemporary Childbirth (19 min: FHS)
Design for Living (26 min; 1990; FHS)
Development and Aging (29 min: 1990; IM)
Genetic Screening (26 min; 1990; FHS)
Genetic Testing (26 min; 1990; FHS)
High Risk Pregnancy (19 min; FHS)
Infertility: Nature's Heartache (28 min; FHS)
Into the World (26 min; 1990: FHS/CARO)
Life from the Lab: Progress and Peril (17 min: 1990; PLP)
Nature and Nuture 52 min; 1990; FHS)
Options for Infertility (19 min; FHS)
Reproduction and Diversity (25 min; 1990; FHS)
Saving Premature Infants (19 min; FHS)
Shares in the Future (26 min; 1990; FHS)
Superanimals, Superhumans? (26 min; 1992; FHS)
The First Year of Life (28 min; 1990; FHS)
The Perfect Baby (60 min; 1990; FHS/PLP)

Films: 16 mm

A Baby is Born (23 min; PE)
Anatomy and Physiology of Pregnancy (10 min; PRI)
Development of Organs (28 min; McG)
Diagnosis of Hidden Congenital Anomalies (10 min; MF)
Fertilization (28 min; McG)
Fertilization. Cleavage and Implantation. (18 min; TF)
Modern Obstetrics-Normal Delivery (28 min; AJN)
Modern Obstetrics—Preeclampsia —Eclampsia (28 min; AJN)
Prenatal Management (8 min; PRI)
Reproduction Among Mammals (11 min; UCEMC)
Resuscitation of the Newborn (25 min; AJN)
Test-Tube Babies (57 min; TLV)
The Beginning of Life (30 min; BNF)
The Thread of Life (54 min; UIFC; KSU)

Transparencies: 35 mm

Life in the Womb, Parts l-2 (160 slides; IBIS)
Prenatal Genetic Diagnosis (20 slides; EIL/CARO)
The Beginning (childbirth) (EIL)
Human Reproduction and Childbirth (40 slides; EIL)
Neonatology Medical Slide Series (218 slides; CARO)
Conception Control; Human Development: Accidents of Development; Mechanisms of Differentiation; Germ Cell Formation and Fertilization (all from H&R)
Meiosis (74 slides; BM)
Genetics, Parts I-III (219 slides; BM)
The Genetic Material (59 slides; BM)
Heredity, Health, and Genetic Disorders, Parts 1-2 (160 slides: IBIS)

Transparencies (for overhead projection)

Mammalian Development (K&E)
Mitosis and Meiosis (36 slides: BM)
Frog Development, Sets l-3 (66 slides; BM)
Pregnancy; Human Male Genital Organs; Hormonal Control of Male Glandular Functions; Human Female Genital Organs; Hormonal Control of Female Glandular Functions; The Menstrual Cycle; Birth;
Multiple Births: Birth Control and Contraceptives; Sterilization and Castration; Venereal Diseases (all CARO)
Genetics: Determination of Sex: Genetics: Red, Green Color-Blindness (both GAF)

Computer Software

Alcohol and Pregnancy (IBM; PLP)
Birth Defects (IBM; ET)
Human Life Processes III: Development and Differentiation (IBM; CARO)
Pregnancy and Health (IBM, Macintosh; PLP)
Pregnant! and Prenatal Baby Care (IBM, Macintosh; EI)
Reproduction, Growth. and Development (IBM, Macintosh; QUEUE)

3. Answers to Illustrations and/or Questions:

Answers to Figure 26.2

1. Primary spermatocyte
2. Secondary spermatocyte
3. Spermatid
4. Sperm cell
5. Spermiogenesis
6. Meiosis

Answers to Figure 26.3

1. Oogonium
2. Primary oocyte
3. Secondary oocyte
4. Second polar body
5. Meiosis

4. Answers to Laboratory Report Questions:

Answers to Part 1. Multiple Choice

1. (c)
2. (b)
3. (d)
4. (a)
5. (c)
6. (a)
7. (b)
8. (c)
9. (a)
10. (b)

Answers to Part 2. Completion

11. 23 (haploid)
12. Crossing over
13. Spermatids
14. Spermiogenesis
15. Placenta
16. Fetus
17. Primary germ layers
18. Extraembryonic coelom
19. Diploid (2n)
20. First
21. Primary
22. Zona pellucida
23. Capacitation
24. Inner cell mass
25. Basalis
26. Seventh